Whatever the weather

Published in 2007 by
Gomer Press, Llandysul, Ceredigion, SA44 4JL
www.gomer.co.uk

ISBN 978 1 84323 821 8

A CIP record for this title is available from the British Library.

This book is published with the financial support
of the Welsh Books Council.

Printed and bound in Wales at
Gomer Press, Llandysul, Ceredigion

Whatever
the
weather

DEREK BROCKWAY

CONTENTS

Foreword

Some boys dream of being a fireman, a footballer or an astronaut when they grow up. Me? I was different; I wanted to be a weatherman. From a very young age I have loved the weather and have always had my head in the clouds. I used to drive my parents bonkers watching all the weather reports on TV. It was always my ambition to be a forecaster but I never thought that I, a shy boy from Barry, would end up working in television and radio.

Being a friendly and approachable kind of guy, I am often stopped in the street by people who want a chat. They ask me about the weather and, of course, are always willing to remind me of the times when I get it wrong. They also want to find out how I became a weatherman and what I do with my time when I'm not broadcasting. Therefore this book is my story; I share memories of my early life growing up in Barry, the highs and lows at the Met Office and how I stumbled into the world of television.

I've been lucky; my passion for the weather has helped me to achieve my dream job, and all along I've had the love and support of my family and friends. It is to them that I wish to dedicate this book. I hope you enjoy reading it as much as I have enjoyed writing it and that it puts a smile on your face. If you ever feel down, remember: whatever the weather, the outlook is bright and the sun is always shining above the clouds!

Derek Brockway

A Passion for Weather

I first became interested in the weather when I was about eight years old. My interest was sparked by the hot summer of 1976 which was a real scorcher and the hottest on record. I've always liked extremes – blizzards, heatwaves, gales, that sort of thing – and there's no doubt that the summer of 1976 was at the extreme edge of weather conditions. But already I'm jumping ahead of myself. I need to go back to the beginning, to when it all began.

In the garden at Hillary Rise

With my sister, Kathryn

I was born on October 29th, 1967 and even at that stage I proved to be a bit of a handful. I was born one month premature and had to spend the first few weeks of my life in an incubator. Mind you, it wasn't my fault that I came early. We used to have a tall kitchen cabinet in the house and my brother, for some reason, decided to climb it. I think he wanted to get some paper that was stored up on the top but, anyway, his weight pulled the whole thing over. Everything smashed, all the cups and crockery, all the bottles of sauce and jam and pickles that Mum kept there, everything all mixed up on the floor. It was the last thing she needed, being eight months pregnant. It really upset her and because Dad was in work, she had to clear up the mess. Result? Me, arriving a month early: I weighed just 5 pounds and 13 ounces.

My father, Cliff, was a Cardiff boy from Cathays. One of eight children, he trained as a plasterer when he left school but for most of his life he worked as a tanker driver for Esso Petroleum based at Ferry Road in Grangetown, and delivered petrol and diesel all over south Wales. He was a good soccer player in his youth but then became ill with pleurisy and was hospitalised for a time at Llangwyfan in Denbighshire. That's where he met my mother, Joan, who came from Barry. She had contracted pneumonia and then pleurisy which left a shadow on her lung, so she had to spend time in the same hospital as Dad. This was in 1949 and they were both in their mid to late teens.

After leaving hospital Mum and Dad returned home and started 'courting' as they called it in those days. Eventually they married in December 1954 and my brother Steven was born two years later. They lived with Nan and Pop, Mum's parents, for a while but eventually moved to a council flat off Gladstone Road. My sister Kathryn was born in 1961. They then moved in February 1964 to a council house in Hillary Rise, Barry, not far from the railway line. That's where I spent all my early years.

I can't really say what my first memory is but I do know I had a dummy until I was about three. Anyway, it was quite a late age. I remember Dad finally taking the thing off me and throwing it into the coal fire we used to have in the living room. I was very upset.

Mum always tells me that I was afraid of thunder. I can remember being on holiday visiting my Aunty Joan and Uncle Alan in Lancaster during the summer of 1975. We had this massive thunderstorm that seemed to go on for ever. I was scared stiff and used to hate

Flat Holm island

seeing the lightning flickering through the curtains. That's strange because now, as a meteorologist, I love to hear thunderstorms overhead; the louder the thunder the better. Mind you, I like strong winds too – and we had lots of them in Barry in those days. As a child I was always hoping to see slates coming off the roof or trees falling down – the action and disaster that appeal to most small boys, I guess.

Living in Barry, we were close to the Bristol Channel and whenever there was thick fog, you could hear the foghorn from Flat Holm island. The noise used to frighten me, so Mum used to put the radio on to help me get off to sleep. Fog was more common in those days because people had coal fires – the soot particles helped to form the fog. I wasn't too keen on the coal trains that used to go past our house either, on their way to Aberthaw power station. They used to rev their engines, and the sound made me think it was a monster coming to get me. It's funny how a child's mind works.

*At a Soroptomists' luncheon in Barry
with Maywin Thomas, former
headmistress of Holton Road School*

From an early age, I always loved snow. I can still remember standing in the street outside our house, looking for the first flake of winter. And when it did finally snow I'd put our dog on a lead and be out of the door quicker than a rat up a drainpipe. That poor dog, I'd take him out in all kinds of weather but he never seemed to mind.

I went to Holton Road Primary and Junior School and really enjoyed my time there. It was a lovely school and I have many happy memories. The teachers were kind – they made you work, but they always had time for you if there was a problem. The headmistress in my time there was Maywin Thomas, who persuaded me not so long ago to make a return visit to Barry, to speak to the Soroptomists. They gave me a very warm welcome.

Another of my old teachers made contact with me recently. Raye Clutton taught me in the last couple of years at Holton Road in the late 1970s and she says that my interest in the weather was obvious, even in those days. We had a chart on the wall, recording weather conditions.

> 'You never let me forget that it needed to be filled in every day. You were in charge of the thermometer out in the school yard and you'd be out there checking it, no matter what the weather was like. Wind, snow or hail, you'd be out there.'

Apparently on one occasion when it snowed, Raye was concerned about getting home to Cardiff in her brown Ford Escort, but all I could think about was getting out and playing in the snow as soon as I could.

'You knew everything about the weather,' she said, 'clouds, temperature, everything. Whatever project we were doing, you'd get the weather in somewhere. Mind you, that wasn't your only interest. I taught Welsh in the school and you were very good at that. It really pleases me when I see you on television now – your pronunciation of all those Welsh villages and towns is excellent.'

It's strange, the things you remember from your school days. When I was in Class 2B I wrote a story about a shipwreck, the survivors all ending up on a desert island. The teacher had it typed and bound up into a book. I never knew until I started gathering material for this book, but Mum kept it – she's still got it. The first paragraph, you could say, rather betrays my choice of future career:

> 'All of a sudden the news came that the ship was sinking. In a quarter of an hour the people were all in the cold sea. It was a very hot day but the sea was still very cold. After about six hours in the sea everybody was like an iceberg.'

A little bit later the story goes on:

> 'Then a very strong wind blew up. It howled frequently and the people got very frightened. The wind blew stronger than ever. It was like a cyclone.'

I don't know if I'd ever have made a Jeffrey Archer but I was fascinated by the weather.

I still remember the blazing hot summer of 1976. The newspapers were full of stories about water shortages and the soaring temperatures and, looking back, I think I probably spent the summer watching the weather forecasts on television. I used to make notes, recording the temperature on a thermometer I had out in the garden and reporting on what the weather had been like too.

There was an old sea captain, Ralph Proud, who used to live in Marine Drive in Barry. He had all the instruments needed to record the weather properly – a Stevenson screen, rain gauge and anemometer. He used to send his records to the library in the town, and really took it seriously. I found his address, got in touch with him and he invited me to his house to see his weather station.

I also remember writing to Jimmy Saville, to the *Jim'll Fix It* programme. I wanted to meet Jack Scott, the BBC weatherman, and asked Jim if he could

> MYSELF
> MY FAVOURITE FOOD is CHIPS 'N BEANS
> MY INTEREST is weather
> WHEN I LEAVE SCHOOL I either
> WANT TO WORK AT THE MET OFFICE
> IN LONDON OR BE a electrician
> I HAVE ONE BROTHER STEVEN
> AND A SISTER KATHRYN

Dydd Gŵyl Dewi at Holton Road

arrange it for me. I wasn't lucky enough to get onto the programme but they passed on my letter to Jack Scott and he actually wrote back to me. That was a real treat for an eight-year-old who was just beginning to develop an interest in the weather.

Mum remembers those years for rather different reasons:

'You were a really mischievous little boy, often up to no good,' she said. 'I can remember the time when you climbed up the lamp-post outside the house, removed the bulb, and swapped it with one from your bedroom lamp. The house lit up like a beacon.'

Later on I went a step further and took all the light bulbs out of the lamps in our street and then watched the man from the electricity board going up and down the road in his van looking for the culprit. The things you do as a child! You don't have much idea of the consequences when you're young. Like the time I was pedalling like mad on my three-wheeler bike, not concentrating on where I was going. Of course, I ran straight into a motorbike and sidecar owned by Mr Lesley Prince, our neighbour, and knocked it down the hill. Away it went, careering down the road, only just missing all the cars parked at the bottom. Mum says the neighbours used to run indoors when they saw me playing in the street!

I think part of the trouble is that I've always had itchy feet, always wanting to be on the go and I am the same now. The only time I would sit still was in front of the television, watching programmes like *Swap Shop*, *Tiswas* or *The Benny Hill Show* and of course, the weather forecast. Otherwise, I was out, exploring, getting involved in things. I was restless, I suppose. When we went on holiday as a family, I'd pester Dad half to death – 'Are we there yet? And where are we going next?'

I was happy if I could be actually working at something. I can still remember the calculator Mum and Dad bought me when I was ten years old. I loved fiddling with things. As a teenager, I decided to re-wire the house, just the lighting circuit, luckily, working from a DIY book. I thought I could do it over a weekend but in the end it took me a week during half-term. I made one mistake and had an electric shock from a neutral wire, would you believe, but after a few adjustments it was all in working order.

Mum has a somewhat different memory about my electrical work, however:

> 'You had a terrible habit of poking screwdrivers into plug points,' she says. 'I had a washing machine with an electric wringer and one day when I plugged it in I had a shock, a real jolt. I screamed and you just flew out of the room. It was a good job I was wearing slippers with rubber soles otherwise I wouldn't be here today! When we got an electrician to check things out he found that the plug had been tampered with. I don't know; you were always messing around with the plugs.'

My reputation as a bit of a mischief-maker followed me around. We went on holiday to Woolacombe in Devon when I was about three and I was so

With my mother in 1993

Hyperactive on holiday

Mum, the goldfish and me

impatient I ran, fully clothed, into the sea. Then, a bit later in the holiday, I went missing for a while. I was off, wandering around. But there was a sudden knocking on the chalet door and when Mum opened it she was confronted by the owner of the holiday park. 'Has your son been near the pool?' he asked. 'Somebody's pulled the plug out and emptied it!' All I can say, quite honestly, is that it wasn't me.

Those early childhood years in Barry were wonderful. There were lots of kids on the estate and we had a great time. We'd play rat-a-tat ginger, knocking on people's doors and then running away. On another occasion, I must have been about eight, two friends and I climbed up onto the railway near Cadoxton Station and threw a stone off a bridge. Unfortunately, it landed on an unmarked police car. We ran off but were caught and had a good telling-off.

On Bonfire Night we always had huge fires on the 'patch'. All the kids mucked in, collecting 'bomber' – wood and things to burn. Mind you, we had to hide it away otherwise gangs from other estates would come and pinch it. We used to do 'Penny for the Guy' as well. Halloween was a great time. 'Trick or treat' wasn't so big in those days and instead of a pumpkin, Dad hollowed out a swede to make a lantern with a face carved on the side. I would carry it around the street with a candle flickering inside.

These were happy times and sometimes I wish I could go back. On a Sunday we would occasionally go to Bessemer Road market in Cardiff and wander around the stalls looking for bargains. Sunday was also a time when the whole family would get together and have tea, watching television programmes like *Black Beauty* and *Upstairs Downstairs*. Mum was always in the kitchen making sandwiches and cakes.

We had lots of pets over the years: three cats called Fluffy, Kim and Sandy; budgies, goldfish, a hamster and two guinea pigs – one called Squeak. And later we had a dog called Chico. The 1970s were a great time to grow up. We weren't well off by any means. We didn't have carpets upstairs for years and in the winter we used to put tape around the windows to keep the draughts out, but most importantly, Mum and Dad were always there for us.

Our house was quite close to Mum's family, in particular her parents, Freda and Bill Lacey. They lived in Gladstone Road in a council house opposite the police station. My grandmother used to buy me little books about the weather, books like the 'I Spy' series that we used to have then. I always called my grandfather Pop and he was a lovely man. Whenever I went round there Pop would always ask, 'Are you hungry?' He loved cooking and was always happy to make a meal, whatever time of day I called, and it was usually my favourite, beans and chips. He always had a large bag of spuds under the stairs and his chip pan was always on the go. Pop used to eat wine gums and would always give me a few. Nan used to make apple tarts and I would always have a slice or two when I visited. Sadly, they are no longer around but I will never forget them. They would do anything for you.

In Junior School I was popular with the girls and regarded lots of them as my friends. Once I went to a birthday party and I was the only boy there. Michelle Hatcher who lived around the corner from Nan and Pop was a good friend. 'I remember once standing on the steps of the school huts discussing cumulus clouds with you,' she said. 'We had to be separated at school for being naughty.' In fact one teacher, Miss Batchelor, described me as 'disruptive' in one school report.

In 1979, aged 11, it was time to leave Holton Road and move onto the big school. Michelle went to Bryn Hafren Girls, I went to Barry Boys' Comprehensive and I didn't see her again for twenty years, which was a great shame. At Holton Road, we'd been pretty much wrapped in cotton wool but it was a different story

Mum and Dad

Nan and Pop at Gladstone Road

Michelle Hatcher and I made a nostalgic visit to Holton Road School

in the comp. The headmaster was very strict and the school was full of boys from all over town. I never really enjoyed my time there and missed the girls. I worked hard and did well at exams which made me a little unpopular. I was called a 'swot' amongst other things and some days I didn't want to go to school. Children can be cruel sometimes, but at the end of the day it's all part of growing up. I wasn't sporty, but did enjoy P.E. My favourite subjects were English, Welsh and geography. I loved learning about different countries and climates. I was good at art, too, but decided to drop this and continue my studies in Welsh. In the sixth form, I joined the Romilly snooker club in Barry. I wasn't much good, though. I think my highest break was 30, if that!

It wasn't until later that I started to take an interest in science, but I was still crazy about the weather, particularly the extremes. And occasionally I was still getting into trouble. One escapade I remember was putting paper down the sewerage inspection pit in the garden and setting it alight. All the smoke went up the stench pipe on the side of the house and the next thing Mum and Dad knew was a retired fireman banging on the door telling them the place was on fire! Recently, I bumped into an old neighbour, Mrs. Romans, and she reminded me of the time I used to reflect the sun into her living room using a mirror in my bedroom. No wonder she kept her curtains closed! Another time, Mum and Dad went out for the evening, leaving me watering the garden with a hosepipe. When they came home, the garden was watered but I had given the outside of the house a good wash as well. Everywhere was soaking.

In the evenings I used to listen regularly to the shipping forecast on Radio Four and then the weather summary after midnight. When I was fourteen I developed a habit of phoning the Met Office in Cardiff, asking questions or talking about the weather. They got used to my voice and said I should come in for a visit. So that's what I did. A forecaster at the Cardiff Weather Centre showed me around, explained what they did and how the equipment worked. I found it fascinating and it fuelled my interest even more.

Barry Boys' Comprehensive

When it came to exams I was successful at GCSE level. I passed eight of them, 5 Bs and 3 Cs and decided to go on to the sixth form and study A Levels. I took maths, physics and geology but by the second year I began to lose interest and motivation. Late adolescence can be a difficult period, though some cope with it better than others. It just wasn't the right time for me to be studying – I needed a break and a change of scenery. In the end I passed maths; we'll draw a discreet line over the other two.

And that was it, my school life was over. I didn't want to go to university and do a degree in maths and physics. I wanted to earn money, so I had to find a job. I applied for a position in the Met Office but my first job was working for the DSS in Barry for seven weeks. In September 1986 a vacancy came up for an Assistant Scientific Officer at the Cardiff Weather Centre. I just couldn't believe my luck. I had always wanted to be a weatherman and when I got the job, my dream of a lifetime had come true!

Out of school at last

Let it Snow

Like most children I loved snow when I was a boy. It was the most exciting time of the winter, those first few moments when you woke in the morning and the bedroom seemed brighter than usual. Instead of traffic noise there was peace and quiet and when you pulled back the curtains you hoped to see everything covered in a thick blanket of snow. If you were lucky, you had a day or more off school. I was always looking out for the first flake and when it started to come down I always hoped it would turn into a big blizzard, the snow whipped up into huge drifts by a strong and biting wind. Just a light dusting was never enough!

Colonel Paterson on the A44 at Llandegley, Brecon

The really big snow of the twentieth century fell before I was a twinkle in my father's eye, in the winter of 1947. This really was an exceptional winter with some dramatic snowstorms. The severe weather didn't start until January 22nd and continued until about March 15th. Snow fell frequently and in large amounts. In the Denbighshire hills depths of level snow reached 1.5m (5ft) with drifts 6m (20ft) deep in places. Talk to anyone about that time and they will tell you stories about battling to work or school through waist-deep snow or walking over the tops of hedges.

Mum was a young girl at the time but she remembers that winter with great clarity:

'It was such a grey and depressing time. It wasn't long after World War II. There were already food and fuel shortages and the severe weather made life even more difficult. No coal was getting through to people's homes because what little there was, they needed it to run power stations and industry. I can still remember my little brother and I walking along the street in Barry, pulling a small truck behind us. We were on our way to the Gas Board to try to get some coke to keep the house warm. The cold was so biting, it went right through to your bones.'

At times, much of the country came to a standstill. Public transport didn't run and in some places people just couldn't get to work. To keep the ports open, the government had to use ice-breakers, more used to working in the Arctic than in Britain. Large parts of the country suffered daily power cuts. Factories were forced to shut down and over four million men found themselves on the dole.

In mid and west Wales, villages were cut off for days on end. The only way to get food and fuel through to some of them was by air, dropped from RAF planes.

John Selwyn was a thirteen-year-old schoolboy living in Llandrindod when the winter of 1947 kicked in with a vengeance:

Middleton Street, Llandrindod Wells, 1947

'The snow was thigh-deep and the wind strong and bitter. Roads were blocked and trains did not run for days. My father and uncle had to walk two miles to a farm to bring back milk for the family in small churns put in rucksacks. The whole countryside was under thick, frozen snow – all the hedges, fences and gates were buried. In the town, snow was cleared with shovels by shopkeepers and piled high in the gutters. Schools closed or opened only for part of the day and the afternoons were spent sledging. The traditional sledge run was The Brifty but it could not be reached because of the deep snow. However we developed our own from the railway bridge at the top of the Crescent down Norton Crescent into the Rock Park and the hotel. It was brilliant and lasted for about a week until the police stopped us. The road became compacted with ice and became impossible to get up or down.'

Farmers across Wales will tell you that the snow of 1947 was the worst in living memory. They lost more animals that year than in any other. Almost a quarter of the country's sheep perished.

In Phil Carradice's book, *Coming Home*, he quotes Eluned Rees of Llansteffan, one of many isolated and cut-off communities, talking about the men of the village digging their way into town to pick up one of the village boys just back from the war:

Vera Webber, her mother and her son, fetching milk through a tunnel of snow

A party of boys fetching milk from the farm at Garndiffaeth

'The people of the village, they thought it was urgent to get to Carmarthen to fetch Dolph – that was Dai's son. And so all the men got into Dai Carrier's lorry and dug their way into town. I don't remember how long it took but I can remember the tension at our end. After all, we didn't know whether they'd made it, whether somebody had fallen off or if the lorry had got stuck. It was quite an anxious time in the village as dusk was approaching.

We were all on the street waiting. I can remember, vividly, a shout going up – "They're coming!" And then we heard the rumble of the lorry and as they came up the hill we were all cheering. I was terribly proud because there was my father, all six foot of him, in his policeman's cloak and hat, brandishing his spade. And they brought Dai Carrier's son back.'

The winter of 1947 was the snowiest since 1814. Just trying to keep warm was an art in itself. Some people had to wear coats and scarves indoors. Others burned their garden fences and packing crates, cut down trees and hedges for fuel. And when the snow drifted it really did lie feet-deep across the land.

Vera Webber of Garndiffaith, Torfaen, remembers how getting food and milk to the village was a priority:

'No traffic could get through as Garndiffaith is all hills, but the train came as far as Abersychan, so each day the men made teams. Our local undertaker made three sledges, two for to go down to the station at Abersychan to collect the most wanted foodstuff, and the third to take the people who had died – to Abersychan slaughterhouse, as they had a large refridgerator. The ground was frozen so no graves would be dug.'

Averil Phillips remembers similar scenes in Pembroke Dock that year:

'We had a wall, just opposite the back door. The wall was perhaps six or seven feet high. Well, when my father-in-law opened the door one morning there was no back yard, just snow. During the night it had come down and filled in the gap between the door and the wall, six feet deep. You couldn't see the wall and the snow was up above the height of the door. My father-in-law had to cut steps into the snow – and it was rock hard, packed solid – just to get out.'

Beacons Road, Brecon, 1947

Overleaf: Colonel Bennet-Evans, Llangurig
(photo: Ken Davies)

The winter of 1962/63 was not as snowy as 1947 but it was colder and went on for much longer. In fact, it was the coldest winter in Wales since 1740! When I talk to people about that time, they say that the snow lay on the ground for two or three months before it finally began to thaw. Football matches and race meetings were called off but one game that did go ahead was the Wales versus England rugby match at the old Arms Park in Cardiff. This was because the ground staff had thought ahead and covered the pitch with straw. Mind you, they probably wished they hadn't bothered. Richard Sharpe, the English outside half, scored one of the memorable tries of the season and Wales lost.

One man I talked to recently has a clear impression of the snow lasting for weeks on end – much to his regret:

'I didn't have a garage in those days and parked my car in the street in front of my house. When it first snowed somebody decided to build two big snow mounds, one in front of my car, the other behind – great fun, they thought. Then it froze and continued to freeze for the next two months. I couldn't move my car, couldn't get it past the lumps of snow. I had to walk to work every day, a four-mile round trip – in those conditions. If I could have got my hands on the bloke who built those snow mounds I think I'd have dug the car out with his head!'

Skating on Bishop's Pond,
Abergwili, 1963

Extremely low temperatures were recorded – for example, a minimum of minus 18°C was recorded at Loggerheads in Denbighshire. Lakes and rivers froze. Huge blocks of ice formed on beaches. The docks at Bristol were almost solid with ice. And some people say the sea froze in Penarth!

Mum and Dad were living in a flat off Buttrills Hill in Barry at that time. Mum says:

> 'Everything froze – and I mean everything. The roads and pavements all turned to sheets of ice. You could hardly get down to the shops to buy food. You'd have to hang on to the railings for dear life – not easy if you're trying to carry a bag of groceries. They managed to keep the roads open. There were tracks in the middle where cars and lorries had been and you drove in those.'

Dad still managed to get into work, as did most men. It was just a case of head down and doing the best you could. We're never prepared for extremes of weather in this country but the determination of individual people still amazes me.

Roy Noble, my fellow broadcaster on BBC Radio Wales, remembers the winter of 1963: 'I was a college student in Cardiff at the time, and Roath Park Lake froze solid for weeks. The ice was so thick, you could walk across the lake and believe it or not, some boys even played "ice rugby" in the middle!'

All over Britain, schools and factories were forced to close at one time or another. Miners couldn't get to the pits and consequently supplies of coal fell by 100,000 tons in just seven days. The small or back roads were impassable for weeks and the diesel in buses and trains actually froze in their tanks.

One of the first snowstorms I can remember as a boy came on February 18th, 1978. The blizzard turned out to be one of the biggest of the century and the worst for fifteen years. In Cardiff there was 34cm of level snow with drifts 8 metres high. Wales had just beaten Scotland at rugby 22 points to 14 at the Arms Park and many people were out celebrating, including Roy Noble.

With Chico the dog in our snowy back garden, 1978

> 'After the rugby we all dashed off to the nearest hostelry for a beverage or two. It was when we emerged that the shock set in; it was snowing heavily. So heavy, in fact, that many people didn't make it home at all. They had to take refuge in hotels, leisure centres and several convivial houses for days on end. Life-long friendships were made. Fortunately, I got home on the last bus that made it to Aberdare. It was touch and go, and such was the camaraderie on the bus, that one fellow from Mountain Ash took his cap off and had a whip-round for the driver.'

Villages were cut off for days by huge snowdrifts. RAF helicopters airlifted 45 people in south Wales and took food supplies to the more rural areas. *The Western Mail* even produced a 'Blizzard Special', selling at just 5p a copy, telling the story of the sudden snow and its effects on people. According to the paper, 300 refugees, many of them like Roy Noble returning from the Wales-Scotland rugby international, were forced to bed down in Cowbridge Town Hall. In Porthcawl the figure was over 600. In Pembrokeshire, farmer Pat Russell found

Snow on Cadoxton mountain

himself stuck in a snowdrift on the Castlemartin firing range and had to be rescued by the army in a tank. The soldiers towed him and his trailer, full of hay, to his isolated herd of cattle and then took him home again – real good Samaritans.

The winter of 1978/9 was the coldest and snowiest since 1963. Hundreds of birds died in the freezing conditions and one of my strongest memories is of Mum coming in from pegging out clothes on the washing line, crying with the cold. Her hands were purple and frozen. The cold was so intense, with a bitter easterly wind direct from Siberia. Pipes froze and we couldn't empty the bath for days.

As children we went sledging, snowballing, all the usual things that kids do when it snows. But that wasn't enough for me; I had to go one better – or worse, depending on how you look at it. I wanted to see how ice formed. So I poured water over the path outside the front and back door of our house and it turned into an ice rink. It was lethal! It was just a bit of fun to me. I simply wanted to see what would happen and, like always, I never considered the consequences of my actions.

The next big blizzard to hit Wales came in January 1982. Traffic on the M4 motorway was brought to a standstill and the roof of Sophia Gardens pavilion in Cardiff collapsed under the sheer weight of snow. John Mason, a geologist and storm chaser who lives in Machynlleth, remembers it well:

'The snow that year was very heavy,' he says. 'I remember driving through the Cambrian Mountains and the main road was reduced to just a single-track passageway. A train on the Cambrian coast line got stuck in the snow and passengers had to be airlifted to safety. Rescue helicopters from RAF Anglesey and Brawdy in Pembrokeshire worked non-stop, taking people to hospital and helping farmers who were trying to stop their animals from freezing to death.'

Mid Wales suffered particularly badly that year. Roads were blocked and schools were closed, some for over a week. A friend of mine, retired geography teacher Phil Charles, recalls:

'It started to snow on the evening of 7th January and didn't stop until lunchtime on Saturday the 9th. That made it the longest period of continual snowfall we'd ever had. Here in Llandrindod Wells drifts were several metres high but out in the country it was much worse.'

RAF Brawdy delivering a patient to St Bride's hospital, 1982

The snow was accompanied by extremely low temperatures so the snow did not melt but lay on the ground for several weeks. In Shropshire temperatures plummeted to minus 26.1° Celsius – the lowest ever recorded in England.

'Llandrindod High School was closed for over a week,' says Phil Charles. 'The trouble was we were low on heating oil which, in those days, was supplied from Newtown. The lorries couldn't get over the hills. The kids thought it was marvellous.'

Christmas 2004, Brecon Beacons

opposite: Carmarthen park, 2006
(photo: Gawain Davies)

Children and weather forecasters – at least somebody likes snow! Mind you, I can't say I'm as fond of it these days as I used to be when I was a boy. It causes far too much disruption. One mention of the 'S' word on radio or television and people start to panic, rushing to the supermarkets to buy bread and milk, leaving the shelves bare. Imagine what would happen if we had another blizzard like the one in 1982. It doesn't bear thinking about! I reckon the whole country would grind to a halt.

Every year, one question I get asked without fail is, 'Are we going to have a white Christmas?' Speculation is big business for the bookmakers. All it takes is one flake of snow to fall on the Met Office roof on December 25th to make it an official white Christmas – the snow doesn't have to settle and even a sleet shower is enough to make the bookies pay out.

Dylan Thomas in *A Child's Christmas In Wales* describes December as being white as Lapland, but snow on Christmas Day is actually quite rare. The idea of a white Christmas dates back to the time of Charles Dickens when snowy Christmases were much more common. Britain was a much colder place back then and in the middle of a 'Little Ice Age' which lasted from about 1550 to 1850. In those days, winters were long and hard; frost fairs were held on the river Thames in London, which used to freeze over most years. Today, snow is most likely to occur in January and February, and sometimes March and April. In fact, snow is more common at Easter than at Christmas. With climate change set to continue, the chances of snow here in Wales in the future will almost certainly diminish. In fact, by 2040 there may be none at all, because winters in Wales are predicted to become milder and wetter. So, just like in Bing Crosby's famous song, a white Christmas may sadly only be the stuff of dreams for future generations. We should make the most of the snowflakes while they still fall.

photo: Jeremy Moore

Extremes

People seem to be fascinated with disaster, when things go wrong or take them by surprise. I guess that's what makes films like *Twister* so popular. Over the years, Wales has been battered by the elements. Snow, floods, storms and heatwaves: you name it, we've had the lot. No two days are ever the same and that's what makes my job so interesting. Our climate is changeable with mild winters and cool summers, while the prevailing south-westerly winds bring plenty of rain in from the Atlantic. But on occasion, the British weather can be a ferocious beast and it doesn't take much for us to start complaining.

*Cumulonimbus clouds over
Llyn Tegid, Bala*

There can be a big variation in the weather from one place to the next. On a day of sunshine and scattered showers it can be fine and sunny on one side of the street and pouring with rain on the other! Microclimates do exist, depending on topography, exposure, soil type and altitude. In general, the higher you live, the cooler, wetter and windier it is, while coastal areas tend to be drier and sunnier with sea breezes. In Wales, most of the rain falls on the hills and mountains, the Brecon Beacons and Snowdonia, while parts of mid, north and east Wales are in a rain-shadow and so are much drier.

Thankfully, most of the time the weather doesn't interfere too much with our everyday lives but that's not always the case. One small dusting of snow and you'd think the end of the world had arrived. A few months of below average rainfall and there's a hosepipe ban. A week of high temperatures and the railway lines start to buckle. The trouble is, events like heavy snow or drought do not happen every day, so we're never prepared, and sometimes we are badly caught out.

These days, summer is my favourite time of the year. I love the hot and humid days when temperatures soar upwards and you can see the moisture building up in the atmosphere. I like to watch the cumulonimbus clouds towering upwards. They're the clouds that produce thunder, lightning and hail and occasionally tornadoes – that's when weather-watching really becomes fascinating. Some people are scared of thunderstorms; I used to be when I was a boy but now I love them. They are nature's way of releasing static energy and sometimes they help to clear the air.

The summer of 1976 was exceptional and the previous year was a hot summer too, with sizzling temperatures. Mind you, in mid Wales, the summer of 1975 did not have a very promising start, far from it in fact. Phil Charles from

Llandrindod Wells remembers its surprises: 'On 2nd June that year, there was snow on the hills. Temperatures had been low for while and then, out of the blue, snow fell. It was unbelievable – snow in June! Who would have thought it? In fact, it is believed to be the first time since July 1888 that snow had fallen so widely and so far south in summer. However, within a week things had completely turned around, temperatures were up in the mid 20's Celsius and the first of two heatwaves had begun. Mind you, this came too late for the farmers, market gardeners and the ordinary men and women who grew vegetables in their back gardens. The snow and frost ruined their crops and plants – you couldn't get runner beans for months afterwards, not for love nor money.'

Peat cracked by severe drought at Nant-y-moch reservoir

In the middle of June 1976 a belt of high pressure from the Azores settled over Britain and, apart from a few interruptions, stayed there until the end of August. This brought endless days of sunshine and soaring temperatures higher than on the Costa del Sol and the Algarve. Thousands flocked to the beaches or to the parks but there was a downside. England and Wales had to endure the most severe drought ever, reservoirs dried up and the government was forced to introduce water rationing. Over one million people had to collect water from standpipes in the street.

It was a time that my mother remembers well:

> 'The water was cut off for up to 17 hours a day. We had to share baths and use the bath water to water the flowers, place bricks in the toilet cistern to save water – and as for washing cars, well, that just didn't happen.'

1976 turned out to the hottest summer for over three centuries, peaking from June 22nd to July 16th. The temperature reached 26° Celsius daily. Even more

Enjoying the sunshine on the beach at Hastings with Pop

remarkable, from June 23rd to July 7th, a period of fifteen consecutive days, the temperature exceeded 32° Celsius (90F) at least somewhere in the country. Plants and flowers shrivelled and died in the heat. Farmers' crops were ruined and elderly people suffered strokes and heart attacks brought on by the heat.

My family went on holiday to Eastbourne that year but I spent most of my time with my eyes and ears glued to the TV, desperate for news of the weather, wondering when things might change. Mum and Dad were amazed at my enthusiasm but encouraged my interest. They even put up with my 'channel-hopping' to find the latest forecast.

In mid Wales Phil Charles watched the heatwave with growing concern:

> 'If it hadn't been for the compensation water running from the Elan valley reservoirs then the river Wye would have run dry; that would have been disastrous for life along the river bank. The Lugg, one of the Wye's main tributaries that joins it at Hereford, did actually dry up. It became just a series of landlocked pools for much of its length.'

The prolonged drought brought another problem when tinder-dry bushes, trees and scrub grass burst into flames. Call-outs to firemen to fight blazes on Welsh heathlands were, at one stage, as high as 100 a day. One particular fire on the Blorenge Mountain above Abergavenny burned for six weeks, covering the nearby town of Blaenavon in thick smoke. A desperate battle also took place in the Radnor Forest in Powys when firemen fought to prevent the flames from engulfing the entire area.

The heatwave started to break on August 26th, just in time for the Bank Holiday weekend – nothing changes, does it? And once it started raining, it didn't stop. In fact, September and October 1976 turned out to be the wettest since 1727!

In a dry year, one very unsettling sight for us in Wales is the reservoir of Llyn Celyn, Tryweryn, when the water falls to a level where the lost village of Capel Celyn is just about visible – families lost their homes in the 1960s and there is

Llyn Celyn in dry weather with remains of buildings exposed

still bitterness over the way development was pushed through by Liverpool Corporation.

Sun, rain, sun . . . but most dramatic of all, high winds. On 28th November, 2006 a tornado hit Bow Street near Aberystwyth. Thankfully no one was injured but more than twenty houses were damaged, trees uprooted and electricity cables brought down. It was recorded as a T4 on the TORRO Tornado Scale; this International Scale is a measuring system that goes from T0 to T10 depending on the size, wind speed and the damage it causes.

Parts of the portakabin were hurled onto the children's playground

(photos: John Mason)

John Mason is a storm chaser and director of the Tornado and Storm Research Organisation (TORRO). He was called to Bow Street soon after the tornado had struck and took these stunning photographs.

'The tornado struck about 1.15am, I arrived there just after nine in the morning and what I saw was a scene of devastation. Chimney stacks were down, roofs stripped, with slates all over the place. A portakabin had been thrown thirty metres in the air and ripped to pieces. One piece was carried almost a kilometre away and was wrapped around a tree. It was as if a bomb had exploded.'

Tornadoes are more common than you might think in the UK. On average we can expect 33 every year, but in 1982 there were 152. In fact, there are more tornadoes per square mile in Britain than in the USA – they are not as destructive but nevertheless can cause serious damage, depending on their size and strength.

Tornadoes form when warm and cold air currents near a thunderstorm come into contact. They don't mix and the air in between them can start to twist and turn, like a skater spinning on ice with their hands above their head. The more they spin, the faster they go, spiralling and spinning until all you can see is a blur. This violently-rotating column of air is called a funnel cloud which describes how the column extends from the base of the cloud like a pipe. Only when it touches the ground can it be called a tornado. Meanwhile, tornadoes which form over the sea are called waterspouts.

Atlantic storm hits the Gower coast

'The Bow Street tornado was quite significant,' says John. 'The strongest recorded tornado we've had in Britain was in Hampshire, measuring T8 on the scale. The one that hit Birmingham in July 2005, injuring 19 people and causing major damage, was a T5. The strongest tornado to hit Wales came on 27th October, 1913, just a few weeks after the Senghenydd pit disaster. It swept up the Taff valley, killing three people and destroying lots of buildings.'

As a member of TORRO, John Mason is often called to the scene of extreme weather events:

'We have a network of several hundred watchers. They range from Met Office people and BBC employees to amateur enthusiasts. We get a report of a tornado or waterspout and we send the nearest person to record and photograph what they can. In the UK, most tornadoes form over the Midlands and southern England. If you get a super cell thunderstorm then the whole of the storm cloud can rotate and that's when a big tornado can form, causing serious damage.'

Hurricanes affect a bigger area than tornadoes and cause devastation and major loss of life. The most deadly storm on record was Hurricane Katrina which destroyed New Orleans in August 2005. Over 1,800 people lost their lives and damage estimated at $80 billion was caused. Tropical storms in the Atlantic are given names by the National Hurricane Centre in Miami and agreed upon by the World Meteorological Organisation. Six lists are used in rotation, with names alternating between male and female. The letters Q, U, X, Y, and Z are not used because few names begin with those letters. The only time a new name

Towering cumulus and cumulonimbus clouds

is added to the list is if a hurricane is very deadly or costly. Then the name is retired and a new name is chosen.

When I give talks on the weather, almost invariably someone will ask me a question about Michael Fish and the great storm that hit southern England in October 1987. Before the storm, Michael Fish started his forecast by saying 'Earlier on today, apparently, a woman rang the BBC and said she heard there was a hurricane on the way. Well, if you're watching, don't worry, there isn't.' He did go on to say, 'The weather will become very windy.'

Michael was right, though the winds were very much stronger than predicted because the storm changed track at short notice. Technically, the great storm of 1987 was not a hurricane. They only form in the tropics where the sea temperature is 27° Celsius or more – nevertheless the storm was very exceptional and the worst since 1703! It killed 19 people and over 15 million trees were blown down, blocking roads and railways, and bringing down electricity and

Stormy sea at Borth near Aberystwyth, Burns Day 1990

telephone lines across southern England. Falling trees and masonry damaged or destroyed buildings and cars. Luckily, the storm struck when most people were in bed; some even slept through it – if it had struck in the daytime, the death toll would have been much higher.

Wales missed the brunt of the storm in 1987 but it was a different story in 1990. On January 25th, a severe Atlantic storm affected a large part of the UK. Wind gusts over 80mph were recorded inland. Damage was estimated to have cost the insurance industry about £2.0 billion, over 3 million trees were felled and 47 people were killed, the largest death toll from a storm since the North Sea Coast Storm Surge on 1st February, 1953 which killed 307 people.

Wales, of course, is used to gales. In 1938, Aberystwyth was hit by one of the worst storms in its history. Houses on the seafront were devastated and part of the pier collapsed during the gales. On Christmas Eve in 1997, north and west Wales was hit by hurricane-force winds reaching 112 mph at Aberdaron on the Llŷn peninsula. However, the strongest gust of all measured at a low-level site was on October 28th, 1989 – 124 mph at Cardiff International Airport. Mark Littlewood, a friend and former observer for the Met Office, was on duty when the storm struck. 'It was a terrifying experience and one which I will never forget. The wind was so strong that the windows of the office were bowing in and out. Part of the airport roof was blown off, landing in the staff car park, and several cars were written off.'

Winter is the time of year when the most extreme weather conditions occur. You only have to read the diaries of Francis Kilvert, who was a curate at Clyro in Powys at the end of the nineteenth century. Time after time, Kivert mentions freezing temperatures, writing at one stage about what has to be one of the strangest baptisms on record:

> 'There was a large christening party from Llwyn Gwilym. The baby was baptised in ice which was broken and swimming about in the font.'

It gets even worse, later on, when Kilvert talks of taking a bath in water that had shards of ice around the rim. Personally I wouldn't have bothered. The thought is enough to send a shiver down your spine!

The trouble with snow and ice is that, sooner or later, it has to melt. The great snow of 1947 was followed by a rapid thaw, heavy rain and widespread flooding. Rainfall in March was over 300% above average and after weeks of frost, the ground was frozen

Ffair-fach, Llandeilo, where homes were flooded many times in the 1950s

hard so the rain and melting water couldn't soak into the ground. Many rivers burst their banks leaving vast areas of Britain under water. Carmarthen was badly flooded and has endured many more floods since. Further up the Tywi valley, at Ffair-fach, Llandeilo, some terraces were regularly flooded in the 1950s. Rhiannon Davies remembers water flowing through the houses in her street several times, with neighbours helping each other to mop up and dry out their homes. Many other parts of Wales have had to put up with similar discomforts.

The floods of February 26th, 1990 caused immense suffering to the people living in Towyn and Kinmel Bay on the north Wales coast. Rod Taylor, a retired teacher from Ruthin who occasionally speaks to me about the weather in Denbighshire, remembers the event well:

> 'A combination of low pressure, a strong onshore wind and high tides caused a major storm surge. The sea defences could not cope and the sea

Dyfi bridge at Machynlleth, with vehicles abandoned to the flood

water rushed inland. Dozens of houses and bungalows were flooded, many of them belonging to retired and elderly people. Lots of caravan parks were washed away as well. It was a huge disaster.'

Many families had to leave their homes and sleep in temporary shelters. The army, police and fire brigade came to help, using boats to ferry people to higher ground.

Josh Powell, 85, a retired science teacher and author from Merthyr Tydfil first became interested in the weather in 1954. He later became involved with the Met Office after a fatality on the mountain above the town. They were looking for people in the Heads of the Valleys to take measurements so Josh set up a weather station at Cwmbargoed. Between 1967 and 1995 he sent his daily reports, one in the morning and evening, by telephone to the Met Office at Rhoose Airport and, later, the Cardiff Weather Centre.

'The Met Office has a code which includes 99 different types of weather,' he told me recently. 'And I reckon I've seen them all up on the hills above Merthyr – apart from sandstorms!'

Merthyr has seen its fair share of floods and Josh remembers them only too well:

'There was a particularly bad one in 1979. The Rhyd y Car cottages, the old miners' cottages that used to stand close by the Taff, were flooded. A culvert burst its banks up on the mountain and the water swept down the river. Merthyr Tydfil has often had to endure floods but that was a nasty event. People were drowned in their own homes. After that the cottages were moved, brick by brick, and re-built at the National History Museum in St. Fagans near Cardiff.'

Cardiff has had its fair share of floods over the years too. When the Springbok rugby team played Wales in 1961 it rained like on the first morning of creation. The river Taff burst its banks and the old Cardiff Arms Park turned into a lake for a while.

Christmas 1979 was ruined by floods for many people living in mid and south Wales. At Treherbert nearly 150mm of rain (6 inches) was recorded on 26th/27th December. Many rivers burst their banks including the Taff in Cardiff. The overflowing river caused thousands of pounds worth of damage to cars and property.

Frank Hennessey, a musician and broadcaster from Cardiff, recorded a song about the floods, entitled 'Grangetown Whale', and has several other stories as well.

Cardiff flood, 1979

'There are many tales about the lighter side of those dark days. One of my favourites concerns a police sergeant and constable attempting to patrol the area around Cowbridge Road in a rowing boat. The water was only about 18 inches deep and the boat became "beached" on the submerged central reservation.

"Hop out and shove us off," says the sergeant to the young copper. But the constable completely vanished – in a foot and half of muddy sludge. Only his helmet was visible. A few moments later the poor chap shot out of the water screaming "help!"

A manhole just below him had been dislodged by the sheer force of the

Floods in my home town of Barry, July 2007

flood water the previous day. The pair were last seen gingerly dragging the boat towards Canton police station to loud applause from local residents who were watching the entertainment from their upstairs window. Let's hope the floods never return.'

Unfortunately, they did return, in the autumn of 2000. Cardiff escaped the worst this time with new flood defences in place, but other parts of Wales were not so lucky. The north-east experienced major flooding when the river Dee reached its highest level since 1946. In one day alone the volunteers of Flint RNLI were called out to 95 rescues. Then, in 2007 came more flooding. The worst affected areas were across the border in Tewkesbury and Gloucester but in Wales, too, flash floods caused people to evacuate their homes.

The thought of a forecast going badly wrong is something that haunts all weather forecasters, including me. I'd love to be right all the time but that's unrealistic and sometimes people do complain. On February 8th, 2007 I was spot on in predicting snow but my luck ran out the next day, which was supposed to be dry. Instead, there was more heavy snow which caused disruption across much of Wales. It was my Michael Fish moment, my biggest error in ten years on television and a day I won't forget in a hurry. I got a lot of stick and had some explaining to do the following morning. Funny isn't it, how people often only remember the times when you get things wrong. So one thing you need in this job is a thick skin, and a sense of humour helps as well!

Meteorology is not a precise science; no forecast is set in stone and things can and do change. The Met Office has one of the most powerful computers in the world but it can never fully represent the complex and chaotic nature of the atmosphere. We don't have enough observations to cover the whole world, especially over the oceans, to build a complete picture of the state of the atmosphere. Therefore, small errors are likely right from the start, so perfect forecasts are impossible. They certainly become less accurate the further ahead the predictions go. Forecasts more than ten days ahead can be useful but they should not be taken too literally. And extreme weather events will always be particularly difficult to predict. Nevertheless, with the advances in technology, forecasts issued by the Met Office are much more reliable than they used to be. In fact, today's three-day forecasts are as accurate as the one-day forecasts were 25 years ago. The Met Office has forecasters working around the clock, 365 days a year, who are constantly monitoring the weather, updating and issuing warnings. At the end of the day, you can only do your best. All things considered, I think we do a useful and worthwhile job which does save lives.

Convective storm and mammatus clouds, Llwyngwril

The Falkland Islands

I had been working at Cardiff Weather Centre for nearly seven years when I was given an exciting opportunity – to go on a five-month detatchment to the Falkland Islands. It was over ten years since the war there ended and, while it wasn't a particularly dangerous place, it was certainly going to be an unforgettable adventure for me. And eight thousand miles from home is about as far as you can ever go!

Former colleague Dave Harrison taking measurements on the roof of Cardiff Weather Centre

I had enjoyed my time at Cardiff Weather Centre which was then a main meteorological office, with quite a few staff including senior forecasters, supervisors and a commercial manager. In those days some charts were still plotted by hand, using two pens taped together, one red, the other black. The forecaster would then draw the charts up adding isobars and so on.

On the roof of the building, there was a weather station including a rain gauge and a Stevenson Screen which housed various instruments such as thermometers. I had to take measurements every hour and, using a special code, write the observation into a book called the Daily Register. We would also collect other reports from around Wales, quality-control them and then send them via computer to the Met Office headquarters in Bracknell. When the weather was bad it was busy but there were quiet moments which would often lead to mischief! A few of us used to throw paper planes out of the window to see how far they would go. If you were lucky one went as far as Cardiff Central railway station! On another occasion I threw a bucket of water out of the twelfth-floor window creating my own shower. It was a miracle no one got soaked on the pavement below.

As the year passed I was told that there was no future in staying as an Assistant Scientific Officer. Technology was taking over and since I wanted to be a forecaster, I had to improve my qualifications. So, in 1989 I started a science course at Pontypridd College, attending one day a week for two years. I passed and then applied to the Met Office to do an HNC in maths, statistics and physics at Reading College of Technology. This was a two-year course, broken up into four blocks, each six weeks long. It was hard work but I was motivated and passed in 1993. Now I had a ticket to become a forecaster! But the next training course was not until 1994 and I couldn't stay in Cardiff because staff levels were being reduced, so that was how I came to be offered a detachment.

The Met Office has offices all over Britain and some overseas too. Most people work at the new headquarters in Exeter but some work at military bases, providing weather information to the RAF and the Army. In May 1993 I packed my bags and set off for the base in the Falklands.

Mum and Dad drove me to RAF Brize Norton in Oxfordshire to catch the plane, their car weighed down with this huge suitcase full of clothes plus a big cardboard box stuffed with books and music; everything apart from the kitchen sink. Mum was tearful. As she told me later:

> 'You'd always lived at home, apart from a few months away at college. We'd always been close – I even worked at Holton Road School as a dinner lady when you were there so we'd never really been apart. Now, for you to be flying 8000 miles to the other side of the world – well, I felt terrible. I missed you even before you got on the plane.'

Copacabana beach – definitely not in the Falklands!

I was feeling just as apprehensive. I was travelling on my own to somewhere far away from home and the work was going to be different as well. I was still a weather observer but had no experience of working with the military before. There would be new things to learn and I did wonder if I would enjoy the experience, whether it would suit me or not.

It was a long flight on a TriStar with a break in the middle. We stopped off halfway at Ascension Island to refuel and stretch our legs. We weren't allowed off the airfield but were ushered into a small compound where you could have a beer. Half an hour later we were in the air again and heading for the Falklands. Everything seemed to be going fine but then all of a sudden the plane changed direction. The weather in the Falklands had taken a turn for the worse and so the captain chose to play it safe and announced he was diverting to Brazil. The next thing I knew we were landing at Rio de Janeiro airport!

The heady heights of Copacabana's Rio Atlantica hotel

Made it!

I'd left Brize Norton expecting to land in the Falkland Islands and now here I was in the carnival capital of the world. Not that I was able to see a lot of it. We were put up in a hotel next to Copacabana beach and I could see the statue of Christ in the distance on the top of the mountain. I would have liked to have gone up there, to take a closer look, but it wasn't possible in the time available. The one thing I remember about Rio was the journey from the airport, passing the shanty towns or *favelas* as they are called locally.

We had come to Rio in a bit of an emergency so I had to share a room with two guys I'd never met before. One of them was in the Royal Navy, the other the RAF. We went out for a meal and ran the gauntlet of the prostitutes on the street, all touting for custom. I was young and impressionable and I guess I was rather shocked by the openness of it all.

I remember ringing Mum that night. She had the shock of her life when I told her I was in Brazil. By the next morning, however, the weather in the Falklands had improved and so we went on our way. It was a shame as I would have liked to have spent more time in Rio, seeing the sights and enjoying the tropical weather!

After landing at RAF Mount Pleasant I collected my luggage and was then taken by Landrover to the accommodation block. The military base is huge and is home to anywhere between 1,000 and 2,000 British military personnel. It has the longest corridor in the world, half a mile long, which links all the barracks and messes together. I was in the Sergeants Mess and it used to take ages to walk to my room down the corridor. Late at night you could often hear shouting from drunken squaddies and I often wondered who I would bump into when I turned the corner, and if I would get back to my room in one piece!

I was one of several weather observers working for the Met Office in the Falklands. One of them I already knew, Gwyn Roberts from New Tredegar. He was from Cardiff Weather Centre as well and had been to the Falklands before so he could show me the ropes. We worked closely with the military, especially Air Traffic Control, supplying up-to-date weather information, warnings and forecasts for the airfield and beyond.

When I left Britain in 1993 it was late spring but in the south Atlantic it was late autumn, heading towards winter. The nights were drawing in, the weather cold

Fun and games with the weather balloon

and changeable. It could swing from one extreme to the other. One minute the air would be thick with snow, visibility would drop so that you couldn't see further than your nose, and I'd put out a warning. But by the time it was issued the snow had passed and you could see for miles again. A wind from the south was the worst, direct from Antarctica and bitterly cold. I'd never experienced anything like it before and was glad I had taken plenty of warm clothes!

One of the jobs I had to do was to launch a weather balloon or radio-sonde. These are vital to weather forecasts and military operations. A small box of sensors and a battery is carried high into the atmosphere by a gas-filled balloon. Information on temperature, wind speed and humidity is then transmitted to a

Not quite safe on a motorbike . . .

receiving station on the ground. Trying to launch a balloon in a gale-force wind was no joke. Sometimes they'd catch an eddy and go bouncing along the runway before bursting a couple of hundred yards away. One of the other Assistant Scientific Officers was Ben Ayton from Yorkshire. He was in his late 50s and working in the Falklands to top up his pension before retirement. I used to laugh when he'd return from trying to launch one of these balloons. After three or more failed attempts he'd be exhausted, cursing and vowing never to do it again.

On 25th June we celebrated 'Fixmas', which stands for Falkland Islands Christmas. I don't think it had any religious significance, just something the military had thought up to remind them of home, given the weather was like December 25th. And it was just like Christmas back home too – we had turkey, stuffing and all the trimmings for lunch!

I worked long shifts to earn overtime pay, but every now and again I had time to myself. The sports facilities were excellent, with a gym, squash courts and swimming pool. Evenings were often spent in the Sergeants Mess where you could play snooker, watch TV or have a few beers. There were also regular quiz nights – it was a really good social scene.

Sometimes, I would go walking along Bertha's Beach or into Wickham Heights. Occasionally some of us would drive the office Landrover to Port Stanley for a day out. The road was rough and bumpy with deep drainage ditches on either side, so you had to be careful and watch your speed. Another time, a few of us went scrambling on motorbikes. It was great fun and because it was off-road I didn't need a licence.

Once in a while, I would get two or three days off in a row known as 'R and R' for rest and recuperation. During this time I would go exploring, visiting some of the deserted islands and remote settlements; wonderful places like Carcass Island and Sea Lion Island. If the military happened to be going there too, and there was room, you could hitch a lift on one of their helicopters. I flew in everything from Chinooks to Sea King helicopters.

You could also fly with the Falkland Islands Government Air Service (FIGAS) who operated small, twin-engine planes, landing on remote airstrips. There were hotels and guest houses, but sometimes I stayed with the locals to experience their way of life. They never charged as long as you took a food parcel; a few good goodies from the Mess kitchen and they were happy. I remember flying to Saunders Island and staying with Biffo Pole-Evans in her farmhouse. She cooked me a joint of mutton. The only trouble was, I don't eat lamb and to disguise the taste I had to smother it with brown sauce! The islanders were a hardy lot – they had to be, given the weather – but they were also kind and considerate.

The Cable and Wireless Landrover

On one occasion my search for adventure almost ended in disaster. I was staying at the Blue Beach Lodge in San Carlos, a guest house run by William and Lynda Anderson from Lancashire. The snow came in thick and fast and the helicopter that was due to pick me up and take me back to the military base couldn't land. I ended up hitching a lift on a Cable and Wireless Landrover. The journey took hours over rough terrain and we got stuck a few times in deep snowdrifts. Meanwhile my boss at the military base was worried sick. He thought I would not make it back alive for my night shift – thankfully I did, much to his relief and mine.

I managed one day to get on a trip to South Georgia on a Hercules C-130 aircraft. Our mission was to do a mail drop for the small army garrison stationed there. Mind you, it wasn't the most pleasant of journeys; I was sat next to the fuel tank and had to wear ear defenders because of the noise from the engines. The weather wasn't the best either; strong winds and turbulence made me feel queasy. But the scenery was spectacular. From the cockpit and windows I could see the old whaling stations, snow-capped mountains and a few icebergs as well.

Above: Rock Hopper Penguins

Below: Striated Caracara

The Falklands are very windswept and have virtually no trees but the wildlife is out of this world. I'd bought myself a new camera before I left the UK and took hundreds of photographs. I had never seen so many different kinds of birds in my life – they were amazing. Albatrosses, cormorants, geese, oystercatchers and penguins; thousands of them all over the place. My favourite was the Rock Hopper Penguin, because it looks like a punk rocker with a tuft of spiky feathers on its head.

Another bird I remember was the Striated Caracara or the Johnny Rook. One day, I was out walking alone and suddenly I was surrounded by several of these birds of prey all swooping down towards me. I must admit to being slightly scared but I think they were just after some chocolate I was carrying in my rucksack. One of my most vivid memories is of being on Sea Lion Island and watching two bull elephant seals fighting on the beach. It was a really vicious affair with lots of blood. On another occasion I came across the remains of a whale, a huge cavern of white bones, just lying on a deserted beach.

I used to enjoy my trips to Port Stanley with its charming houses and shops overlooking the harbour, most of them with brightly painted corrugated iron roofs. The wooden churches were beautiful too and the cathedral has an arch made from the jaw bones of four whales.

I went to many other places during my time on the Falklands, including Darwin and Goose Green where many soldiers fought and died during the conflict. I visited the graveyard where Colonel 'H' Jones is buried and also the Argentine cemetery. I felt very sad when I saw all the graves. Although it was over ten years since the war, there were still minefields which hadn't been cleared so you had to be careful where you went.

We used to look forward to seeing the Tristar, the 'Big White Bird' as we called it, landing on the runway in front of the Met Office. Everyone was pleased because it meant new people and mail from home. I used to write to family and friends using 'blueys', aerograms used by the British Forces Post Office. It was always nice to get post because although I did telephone home every now and again, it was expensive.

After five months my tour of duty came to an end and it was time for me to board the TriStar and head back home to the UK. I spent a fortnight on leave and went walking. I climbed Snowdon and Cadair Idris and then returned to the Falklands for a short second tour. My forecasting course was postponed so I had the opportunity of coming back and seeing the islands in the summer months. It was still windy but there were some fine and warm days as well. If the wind direction was right, temperatures could rise into the low 20°s Celsius – a big change from those chilling winds from the South Pole!

My second tour came to an end in February 1994 and this time I came home for good. I ended up back at Cardiff Weather Centre and spent most of my time making pots of tea! One thing was sure; it was all very different from the Falkland Islands. Looking back, it was a great experience and if I had the chance, I would return and see the penguins again.

Cathedral at Port Stanley

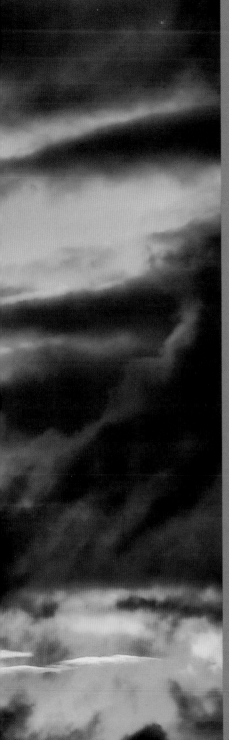

photo: Mike Davies

History of Weather

People have been trying to predict the weather for centuries. In the past, farmers, sailors and others didn't have the luxury of super computers, radar and satellites. They had to rely on more natural methods, such as watching the sky and studying the behaviour of birds, animals, plants and insects. Some of their predictions were based on weather lore passed down from generation to generation and captured in easy and memorable sayings such as 'Red sky at night, shepherds delight.'

A delight for Gower sailors

In Britain, there are around 3000 weather proverbs and many are hundreds of years old, passed down to us from our grandparents. Many of these proverbs or old sayings are little more than rhymes, remembered more for their sound than their meaning. Many are based on superstition but some, especially those based on direct observation of cloud patterns and wind direction, are close to the truth and can be useful to predict the weather in the short term at least.

Probably the most famous, and definitely one of my favourite sayings, is 'Red sky at night, shepherds delight. Red sky in the morning, shepherd's warning'.

This one really has stood the test of time. In fact, it's been around for thousands of years and is even quoted in the Bible! In the book of Matthew, Jesus says to a group of fishermen, 'When it is evening, you say, "It will be fair weather, for the sky is red," and in the morning, "It will be stormy today, for the sky is red and threatening".'

A similar version of the same proverb is applied to sailors:

'Red sky in the morning, sailors take warning.
Red sky at night, sailors delight.'

A red sky at night, when the sun is setting in the west, is caused by light passing through dust and pollution in the lower atmosphere. These particles scatter away some of the light, leaving only the orange and red part of the spectrum. Dust in the air means dry weather and since most of our weather comes in from the west, a red sky is a good sign of fine weather the next day. However, the opposite is true when there is a red sky in the morning. As the sun rises in the east it shines on high clouds in the west. These clouds can be the first signs of a warm front in the Atlantic which may bring rain. So the saying has a lot of truth – but is not always right.

Idris Jones from Llanwrtyd Wells is a farmer so for him the weather is important, if not vital, especially during the lambing season. 'If it's cold, wet and windy the newborn lambs can die of hypothermia. If I see sheep coming down off the mountain that is a sign of bad weather. Perhaps they can sense the air pressure falling, which often precedes rain.'

Idris may be right. Animals are sensitive to changes in the weather and many local beliefs based on animal behaviour have been around for generations. Apparently, when the rooster goes crowing to bed, he will rise with a watery head. If the bull leads the cows to pasture, expect rain; if the cows precede the bull, the weather will be uncertain. When dogs eat grass, rain and severe weather may be on the way.

Twm Elias from Maentwrog is a senior lecturer at Plas Tan y Bwlch (the Snowdonia National Park Study Centre). He is also an expert in weather lore and has loads of sayings up his sleeve. Some I've never heard of before! I'm indebted to him for the numerous beliefs and sayings from all over Wales which I'm able to share with you in the next couple of pages.

Walking with the expert, Twm Elias

Many expect the best weather in any month to be around the full moon. And the shape or slant of a new moon can be seen as a sign of the weather to come. If it is lying on its back like a ship or a bowl, it will be a dry month. That is, the moon catches the water if it rains. But if it's on its side, like a pouring bowl, then it will be a wet month.

Years ago, people used to keep a leech in a bottle filled to the halfway mark with water and use it like a barometer. If the leech got to the top, rain was on its way. But if it stayed still in the bottom it would be fine. Before strong winds, the leech would move quickly in the water wheras it would move slowly or stay in one place in cold weather. If it would come out of the water and curl on the side of the bottle, a storm was on its way.

Beaumaris

There are many local sayings, for example in western parts of Anglesey, if people could see Yr Eifl in the south-west (a mountain on the Llŷn peninsula) they would have dry days but if Yr Eifl was wearing a 'cap' then it would rain before the end of the day. Another humorous variant of this saying is that if you can see Yr Eifl it is going to rain, and if you can't, then it is raining already!

In Beaumaris, a wind from Bangor will bring rain while an east wind from Llandudno will bring fair weather. In Llanelli, fog from the north means fair days. If you can smell the BP refinery, the wind is from the south which means rain! In Llanelidan, a red sunset towards the north means rain the next day. In Mold, a dark sky towards Chester means thunder. The same is true for Ruthin if the sky is dark towards Mold. In Corwen, a full moon in winter means cold, frosty weather. In Llanfwrog, a moon rising red in summer means heat and drought. In St. Asaph, if a cockerel crows at night it will rain before dawn. While in Llandyrnog, rain is imminent if you see a red squirrel crossing the road!

In south Wales, cats rushing through a house in Porthcawl means rain and wind. In the Rhondda valley a storm is brewing if sheep come down from the mountains and the same is true in Merthyr Tydfil – but there, instead of sheep it's ponies. If the sea in Penarth is the same colour as the sky it's a sign of good weather but if it's grey and the sky is blue then unsettled weather is on the way. If the sound of aeroplanes landing and taking-off from Cardiff International Airport is clearer than usual, people in Barry and Penarth know rain is on its way.

In south-west Wales, a sign of rain is when horses turn their backs to the hedge. A sow lying in the mud means warm weather. While if you can see Ireland from the Preseli Mountains, rain is on the way.

In north Wales, hens roosting early in Bala is a sign of very warm weather. In Abersoch, fisherman say if there are big catches of cod in the summer, and the cod arrive earlier than expected, then the sea is colder and the winter could be hard.

A widely held belief in many parts of Wales is that a heron seen flying upstream is a sign of rain – it is thought that he is going upstream 'to open the floodgates'.

In Cardigan Bay porpoises moving north are a sign of good weather to come but moving south, they are a sign that the weather is going to deteriorate.

Big cumulonimbus storm clouds are sometimes called 'Esgobion Bangor' (the 'Bishops of Bangor') by Anglesey people or 'Byddigions Cricieth' (Criccieth gentry) in Meirionydd. These big, fat, bombastic characters are thought to have been on a drinking spree and will soon come and pee all over us!

In parts of Carmarthen and Glamorgan, rain-bearing clouds from the south or south-west are called 'Swansea Jacks'.

If frogs are very yellow in summer it is a sign of sunny weather, but if they are dark in colour watch out for clouds and rain. Talking of rain, the peacock's call is a loud 'glaw! glaw!' and since this is the Welsh word for rain – *glaw* – it is often called '*aderyn y glaw*' or rain bird, and its call evokes wet weather.

Large flocks of starlings, fieldfare or redwing often arrive in early winter just ahead of a snowstorm. For that reason they have earned the Welsh name '*adar yr eira*' or snow birds. Pigs are very sensitive to the weather as well. They love wallowing in mud on hot sunny days, but if you hear them squealing, and it's not feeding time, then prepare for a storm. Before gales they will even carry extra straw for bedding into their sty.

A frog as yellow as sunshine

Overleaf: low cloud in the Tywi Valley

Prancing lambs mean windy weather

Cattle on the summit of a hill or standing up to their knees in a lake or river are usually a sign of hot, settled weather. If cats sit with their backs to the fire in winter, then snow is on the way. Cats become very playful and lambs prance more than usual if the wind is beginning to rise. This also affects humans – ask any teachers and they will confirm that school-children become more unruly during windy weather. So if you want your children to behave, pray for calm weather!

The weather can certainly affect the way we feel, and when damp, cold weather is expected, some people experience aches and pains. During changeable weather, rheumatism and arthritis can get worse as falling and rising air pressure can affect the fluid in our joints, causing real discomfort.

There are many seasonal beliefs too. According to Twm, 'A mild winter in the past was disliked as it was likely to mean a poor summer. For example, February – *mis bach, mawr ei anghysuron*, which means the "small month, big in its discomforts"; if it was mild, then people feared it would "spoil" the other eleven.'

A dry spell in March was much appreciated – 'a handful of March dust is worth its weight in gold'; that is, there would be excellent weather for the harvest.

There are many interesting sayings in the Welsh language such as '*Mae'n bwrw hen wragedd a ffyn*' – which means it's raining old women and sticks! The big bubbles which appear on the surface of water when it is really chucking it down with rain are called '*llygaid yr ych*' – ox eyes. And to describe hail, '*Mae dyn y clocsiau ar y to*' – the clog dancer is on the roof!

There are also some fine stories relating to extreme weather. One of my favourites is about a summer in the 1920s which was so hot that pigs melted into pools of fat in their sties and chickens had to be fed ice-cream to prevent them from laying boiled eggs! In Rhandir-mwyn in the winter of 1895 it was so cold that a sheep which jumped into the air froze and remained suspended there until the spring! Blimey.

I have often heard the saying 'Rain before seven, fine by eleven'. This is

Cartoonist Cen Williams in Golwg *imagined I might be overwhelmed by 'old women and sticks' at book-signings!*

based on a standard weather front that is usually moving in from the west. A typical front lasts three to four hours so, if it's raining at 7am then the front will probably have passed through by 11am and the rest of the day will be fine. This saying is right about 66% per cent of the time but showers *can* follow – so keep a brolly handy just in case!

There's an old Pembrokeshire saying that I particularly like:

Fog on the hill
Brings water to the mill.
Fog on the moor
Brings sun to the door.

Once again there is a degree of truth behind that rhyme. Fog gathering on a hilltop is sign of cloud and moisture and perhaps rain. When it gathers on a moor or on any piece of flat land then that is an indication of high pressure and settled weather.

'If the moon rises with a halo round, soon we'll tread on deluged ground.'

May blossom

There is some truth in this one as well. If you see a halo or circle around the moon or sun then expect rain within 24 hours. The effect is caused by high level clouds such as cirrus which contain ice crystals and they may indicate that a warm front is on the way. This is accurate about 65% of the time.

Being a weatherman, I am often teased about using seaweed and pine cones in my forecasts, but actually pine cones are one of the most reliable of all natural weather indicators. They respond to changes in humidity. In dry weather, they open out but closed cones suggest rain, drizzle or fog. As for seaweed, well it does have its uses. In fine weather it shrivels up and feels dry, but if rain is in the air, it becomes damp and swollen.

One saying I hear every spring is:

> Ash before the oak, then we shall have a summer soak.
> Oak before the ash, the summer comes with nary a splash.

This suggests that if the ash tree has leaves before the oak tree, then a fine summer can be expected. However, in reality it is not that straightforward. Which tree comes into leaf first depends on the weather in the spring. If it's mild and wet, there is a fair race between the two trees but if the spring is warm and dry, the oak tends to comes out before the ash – which is happening more often these days because of climate change.

Plants, and flowers in particular, can help predict the weather. The scarlet pimpernel, which is also called the 'poor man's weather glass', has its flowers open in sunny weather, but when rain is expected they close to protect the pollen. The trouble is, the petals also close at night and in mist or fog when the weather is dry. So it can be misleading.

An old English proverb says, 'Ne'er cast a clout till May be out.' Clout means an article of clothing, while May refers to the mayflower or hawthorn blossom. In other words, wait until the hawthorn tree is flowering before stripping off because winter could have a sting in its tail and catch you out.

The saying 'Swallows high, staying dry; swallows low, wet will blow' does have some scientific basis. During fine, warm weather, the insects that the birds feed on are carried high on warm air currents rising from the ground. However, when the weather is cool and unsettled, the insects stay closer to the ground and so the swallows fly lower too in search of their lunch!

Bees are sensitive to changes in the weather and can help predict the approach of rain. When there is a storm they are unlikely to swarm and stay close to their hives. Spiders are said to leave their webs before the onset of rain.

Damselfly, beautiful in any weather

Cows lying down in a field in the morning are supposed to be a sign of rain. John Moreton, a retired meteorologist in Nottinghamshire, reckons there is some truth in this. 'Before rain, the humidity rises and this attracts more flies so the cows lie down to avoid them.' Others say the cows lie down to keep the ground beneath them dry. The trouble is, what if half the cows are standing, does that mean scattered showers?

Some weather lore is known to be correct such as 'Mares' tails and mackerel scales make tall ships take in their sails.' 'Mackerel sky' is a popular term for a sky filled with cirrocumulus or altocumulus clouds. The pattern resembles the scale on a mackerel fish and it is a sign of a change in the weather with rain and strong winds on the way.

You've probably heard of St Swithin and the belief that if it rains on St Swithin's Day (15th July) then it will rain for the next forty days; if it is fine, it will be fine for the next forty days. According to the Met Office there is no such pattern. St Swithin was an Anglo-Saxon Bishop of Winchester and legend says that as he lay on his deathbed he asked to be buried in a churchyard where the 'sweet rain of heaven' could fall on his grave. His wishes were followed but then later his remains were moved to a shrine inside Winchester cathedral. Apparently, there was a huge storm and it rained for forty days solid, a sign that St. Swithin was unhappy about his new resting place.

I do love some of the old sayings, mind you. 'It's cold enough to freeze the

Weather vane for England as well as Wales – on Offa's Dyke

balls off a brass monkey' is a funny one. Now that has got absolutely nothing to do with what you're thinking. A brass monkey was a triangular frame used on decks of old wooden battleships to store cannonballs. When it froze, the brass contracted and the cannonballs simply fell off; hence the saying.

'It's raining cats and dogs,' Pop used to say. There are many recorded instances of frogs and other creatures falling from the sky but cats and dogs? Actually there are several theories about this saying but the one I like the most comes from medieval times in Britain when there were open sewage ditches running through the towns. Dozens of stray cats and dogs lived in and along the edges of these ditches and, when it rained heavily, the water backed up and they were simply drowned and washed away. To the superstitious people of the time it was, quite literally, raining cats and dogs.

Old weather lore, though it has to be taken with a pinch of salt, does show how humans through the ages have tried to predict the weather. Indeed, meteorology may well have been the first science. In 650 BC, the Babylonians analysed cloud patterns. In the 4th century Hippocrates, the father of medicine, observed that 'whoever wishes to pursue the science of medicine must first investigate the seasons of the year and what occurs in them'. By 300 BC, the Chinese had developed a calendar which divided the year into festivals, each having its own type of weather. In about 340 BC, Aristotle described weather patterns in *Meteorologica*, which led to the term 'meteorology'. He was spot on with some of his observations, but not with others, such as the assumption that everything in the world was made up of four elements – earth, water, air and fire. When all four elements existed in harmony, he argued, the world was peaceful and people could go about their daily lives without fear of natural disaster. However, when one of the elements became too strong, it led to disease, depression and, crucially, bad weather.

To some extent that was a comforting idea. No matter how bad things were you knew that, eventually, the situation would improve; you just had to ride the storm. Astrology and superstition, rather than hard scientific fact, were the order of the day in the medieval world. Apparently, one renowned Elizabethan astrologer announced that the best way to stop lightning striking your garden was to lay out the hide of a hippopotamus alongside a speckled toad and an owl with outstretched wings. No problem then!

During the Renaissance things began to change, with fresh ideas and the invention of meteorological instruments such as the thermometer and the barometer. During the 17th and 18th centuries the accuracy of weather observations improved and was helped by the invention of the telegraph in 1837 which allowed weather information to be transmitted from one place to another and exchanged.

Royal Charter

The Met Office was founded in 1854 by Captain Robert FitzRoy to provide weather information to sailors. Four years later, one of the most terrible storms ever to hit the British coast is still known as 'The Royal Charter Gale' after a ship of that name was driven onto the rocks near Moelfre on Anglesey on the night of 25th October, 1859.

Returning from Australia with 500 passengers, mostly miners and gold worth over £300,000, the ship was literally pounded to pieces by the waves and over 450 people lost their lives. As the storm lashed Britain a total of 133 ships were sunk. The disaster led to the introduction of the first gale warning service by Robert FitzRoy in 1860 to prevent similar tragedies. His daily forecasts were published in *The Times* newspaper but his methods were ridiculed and, sadly, in 1865, he committed suicide.

The truth is, our weather is often unpredictable and history is littered with stories about how storms, gales and summer droughts upset or aided the carefully laid plans of invaders and politicians alike.

Julius Caesar made his first attempt to invade Britain in 55 BC but strong north-westerly winds made his army give up. Nearly a hundred years later

Stormy sea, Porthcawl – enough to deter any invaders

Emperor Claudius sent another army to have a go. This time the weather was better and Britain under Roman rule began.

The one date in British history that most people remember from their school days is 1066. That was the year William the Conqueror invaded Britain, defeating King Harold at the Battle of Hastings and seizing the English crown. The weather played a crucial part in William's victory. Winds from the north had kept his fleet in port around the Normandy coast for several weeks. King Harold, waiting for the invasion in London, was gleefully aware of this. Then news came that Harold had dreaded – another invasion had taken place. Viking warriors under Tostig and Harald Hardrada had landed in Northumberland. Knowing William was still marooned in Normandy, Harold gathered his troops, marched north and defeated the Vikings at the Battle of Stamford Bridge. The day after the battle, Harold received the news that the wind in the English Channel had changed. William had sailed and landed at Hastings. Harold was forced to march rapidly south and fight his second battle, with exhausted troops and little hope of victory.

During the Spanish Armada in 1588 only two Spanish ships were lost to English guns during the whole campaign. The rest were sunk by storms that battered the coast of Britain. Queen Elizabeth certainly knew the weather had saved her country. She had a medal cast to commemorate the victory. On it were the words: 'God blew and they were scattered'.

The great flood of January 30th, 1607 was a huge disaster which hit south Wales. A huge wall of water swept up the Bristol Channel, killing 2000 people; houses were destroyed and horses, sheep and cattle washed away. Eyewitness accounts of the flood tell of 'huge and mighty hills of water' advancing at a speed 'faster than a greyhound can run'. The water reached a speed of 30mph and a height of 25ft. It swept up to four miles inland, affecting Pembrokeshire, Glamorgan, Monmouthshire, Cardiff and Newport. The flood may have been caused by a massive storm surge formed by a combination of high tides and hurricane-force winds. However, some believe the flood was caused by a tsunami, triggered by an earthquake near south-west Ireland.

The Great Fire of London was another tragedy made worse by the weather. A drought during 1665 and 1666 had left the wooden buildings as dry as tinder wood. When the fire started, a strong easterly wind fanned the flames, making it quicker for the fire to spread. The fire destroyed thousands of houses and public buildings, including St Paul's Cathedral.

In November 1703, Britain's worst ever storm, known as the Great Storm, destroyed many towns and structures, including Eddystone Lighthouse. The wind blew at more than hurricane force. At least 123 people were killed on land, while at sea 8000 men may have drowned. Churches were destroyed and over 400 windmills wrecked by the storm.

The Irish famine of 1846 caused untold suffering and death. The famine was partly due to potato blight. A very wet autumn had destroyed the potato crop and this was followed by a severe winter. Hundreds of thousands of people died of starvation or disease and the famine forced many Irish to emigrate.

The Normandy D-Day landings were very dependent on conditions in the English Channel. The weather on June 4th, 1944 took a turn for the worse so the invasion was delayed. Better weather was forecast for 48 hours later, the invasion went ahead and the rest, as they say, is history!

There is no doubt that weather and history are linked. Thankfully, with modern technology we are now better equipped to warn people when trouble is brewing. However, I am sure Mother Nature will continue to affect our lives and ambitions. After all, you can control your own actions, but you cannot hope to control the weather!

Eddystone lighthouse, destroyed in the Great Storm, 1703

Radio and TV

Starting to work in television was a huge learning curve for me. In the early days I had to prepare TV weather graphics, produce the ITV national weather slot, write scripts for Channel Four and brief presenters such as Siân Lloyd, Femi Oke, Sally Meen and Simon Biagi. There were tight deadlines and everything had to be ready on time. I remember one occasion when I was meant to be changing the charts for the GMTV presenter but I fell asleep! It was towards the end of a night shift and I was very tired. Thankfully, they had a sense of humour and forgave me.

Students at the Met Office college

Luckily, by then, I had been on the forecasters' training course, which had included mock radio and television bulletins and all kinds of presentations.

When I had returned from the Falklands, my old job at Cardiff Weather Centre no longer existed, so the Met Office found me a slot as an observer at Birmingham Airport. It was a temporary posting, and I still wanted to train as a forecaster, so when I was offered a place on the course in January 1995, I jumped at the chance.

The course, like my HNC, took place in Reading at the Met Office College in Shinfield Park. It was five months of hard work, hours spent in the classroom learning about meteorology and there were some tough exams as well. Occasionally we split into groups and had tasks to complete and we even had a mock weather office, where we would take on different rôles and prepare forecasts.

There were people from all over Britain and Europe on the course; two from Belgium, one from Switzerland and three guys from Gibraltar. We all got on well and like most students had a few wild parties which often led to a sore head the next day. I worked hard and was pleased to come second out of fifteen in the class. Anyway, that was it, I had finished the course and decided that I wanted to go back to Birmingham for my-on-the job training. However, before starting work I felt I would take some time out.

I took a month off and spent it travelling around Europe by train. The experience of the Falkland Islands had given me an interest in travel and I wanted to see more of the world. I went all over, visiting Bruges, Cologne, Berlin, Prague, Budapest, Vienna, Florence and Nice. I had a great time but I couldn't travel for ever and after a month I went back to Birmingham to start my job as a forecaster. It was good to go back and see my colleagues again and the Brummies are a friendly lot. This time, however, I was working at the weather centre near the NEC and in five months I learned a great deal.

You can study all the theory you like at college or university, but it doesn't prepare you for actually doing the job in the real world. The work at Birmingham was varied with many customers, such as the electricity and gas boards, balloonists and local councils. I had to work 12-hour shifts, by day from 8am until 8pm or the night shift from 8pm to 8am. There were tight deadlines and for someone new to the job it was easy to fall behind schedule, especially if the weather was bad. I also had my first taste of live radio at Birmingham, broadcasting on several stations: BBC West Midlands, Nottinghamshire, Derbyshire, Shropshire, Oxford and Radio Lincolnshire as well.

Lighter moments for the Met Office football team

'We were all very pleased and proud,' says Mum. 'You'd had this ambition to be a weatherman almost all your life and now you'd achieved it. We didn't know at the time, of course, that there was more to come, a lot more.'

During my time at Birmingham, I saw a job advertised in the Met Office circulars for a forecaster at the ITV studios in London. I applied, went for an interview and to both my surprise and delight was offered the job. I was apprehensive about moving to London but at the same time excited about the prospect of entering the world of television. I started work in London in December 1995.

Most of my work was behind the scenes but part of the job involved being a back-up presenter for GMTV. A former Thames Television producer gave me some training. He showed me how to how to stand in front of the camera and how to talk. Siân Lloyd gave me a few helpful tips as well, although I could never quite manage her hand gestures! My first broadcast on GMTV was at 8am on a Sunday in September 1996, right at the end of a night shift. Alistair Stewart was presenter of the programme and he handed over to me. The broadcast lasted for

One of my first broadcasts on national TV in 1996 – feeling and looking a bit nervous

about 90 seconds and I was very nervous to be on national television. Mind you, I doubt whether many people saw me on a Sunday morning; most people were tucked-up in bed and it was probably just as well!

Overall I did about half a dozen broadcasts on GMTV but towards the end of 1996 things began to go pear-shaped. I had some good times in London, made a few friends but in some ways I was naïve. When I first arrived in London I was full of ambition but by the end of the year I wondered whether it had all been worth it. I think I put myself under too much pressure too soon in my career. I was still a relatively new forecaster, still learning my trade, and the added pressure of live TV all became too much in the end. The work involved a lot of night shifts too, up to eleven hours long and often working alone, which I hated. I can remember getting the train home to Charlton from Waterloo and thinking to myself, *What on earth am I doing? I'm slowly killing myself.* The night shifts began to take their toll; I never slept very well after them so my body clock was all over the place. I became unwell, exhausted and eventually had to take some time off.

I was off work for several weeks and took a holiday to Malta which gave me a chance to rest, sort myself out and decide what I wanted to do in the future. I felt disappointed that things hadn't worked out in London but my health had to come first. Mind you, I didn't want to be out of the loop for too long and to ease myself back into things, the Met Office offered me a temporary job as an Environmental Consultant at their headquarters in Bracknell. I was a kind of a salesmen and had to deal with a variety of customers, supply them with past weather data, send out contracts and invoices as well. The good thing about this job was that there were no night shifts. It was 9 to 5, Monday to Friday, work.

I enjoyed my time in Bracknell and thought I would stay there for some considerable time. It was the place to be if you wanted to get promotion. I considered a couple of jobs in computing and sales but nothing really appealed. However, fate had a hand to play. In the summer of 1997 I came back to Wales to see my parents and happened to pop into the Cardiff office one day to say hello to my old colleagues. And while I was there somebody told me that Helen Willetts, the BBC Wales weather forecaster at the time, was moving to London on promotion and a replacement was needed fairly quickly.

Mark O'Callaghan was editor of the *Wales Today* news programme back then. He'd looked at several people from the Cardiff Weather Centre and decided they weren't quite what he was looking for. So when I said I might be interested I was invited to do a screen test. I wasn't really sure about it. I thought my future was at Bracknell and hadn't really considered coming back to Wales to live, let alone work as a forecaster again. I gave it some thought and decided I had nothing to lose, so I sat in front of a camera set up on the wall of the Met Office, smiled and gave a short weather forecast. I mentioned a few Welsh town names to show that I could pronounce them correctly and it must have done the trick because they offered me the job! It was as simple as that; no formal interview or anything. Like a lot of things in life, it was a case of being in the right place at the right time, although being a local boy and a trained meteorologist must have helped as well. I was later told that Mark O'Callaghan thought I could be the Welsh equivalent of Dale Winton! I am not sure whether to take that as a compliment or not, but I am very grateful to Mark for giving me the chance to work on the top TV news programme in Wales.

I started working for BBC Wales in September 1997 and from that point on my life changed. I can still remember my first broadcast on Welsh television; I was nervous, a bit wooden and scared I would forget my lines. It was a case of sink or swim, and there were days when I thought to myself, am I in the right job? Mind you, it would have been too easy to throw in the towel and so I persevered in the hope that it would get easier. Like most things in life, the more practice you have the more confident you become. Even now, though, there are occasions when I would prefer not to go in front of the camera but I have a job to do, so I put on an act, smile and hope the forecast is right!

Live from Cardiff Weather Centre

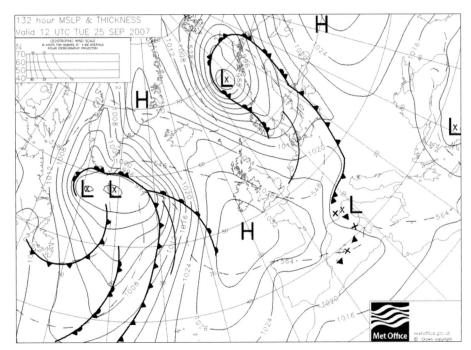

132 hour MSLP & THICKNESS
Valid 12 UTC TUE 25 SEP 2007

Weather charts which are now available on-line

All of my early broadcasts were from the Cardiff Weather Centre with a satellite link to the BBC. Radio bulletins were done from a broom cupboard converted into a studio. For television, I used to sit behind a desk and look at a camera on the wall. It wasn't very natural, though; I couldn't point at a map and I had to rely on someone at the other end to change my charts – far from ideal! In the early days, there were only three radio broadcasts in the day and two on television. There's an awful lot more now, of course.

After a while, they decided to move me up to the BBC Headquarters in Llandaf. I wasn't too keen on the idea at first as I enjoyed working at the weather centre with the other forecasters. It took me a while to settle in but I'm glad I made the move. I feel much more part of the team and work more closely with the news department and Radio Wales staff. It's easier to get to know people and build relationships with other presenters – some of them even performed a song about me entitled 'Who the heck is Derek?' written by Natalie Ball from Cwmparc, who came up with the idea for Children in Need in 2005. There are plenty of 'lighter moments' for the whole team, such as dressing up for Comic Relief events.

Even though I work at BBC Wales, people are surprised when I tell them that I am a civil servant, a meteorologist employed by the Met Office. So, forget the huge salary! However, I do get a clothing allowance and a government pension – not to be sniffed at. As the Met Office is part of the Ministry of Defence or MoD, I had to sign the Official Secrets Act and if I worked as a forecaster for the RAF I would be a Flight Lieutenant.

WALES on SUNDAY   November 13, 2005   **11**

NEW KID ON THE BROCK!

Weather-crazy lad inspires charity 'Derek' song

DEREK, Derek, who the heck is Derek?

If you don't know the answer to that question, you soon will!

A comedy song has been penned paying tribute to BBC Wales weatherman Derek Brockway, whose lively forecasting is cult viewing across the nation.

While the Tribe of Toffs sang John Ketley is a Weatherman in 1988, reaching number 21 in the charts, Derek's ditty has been created especially for Children In Need.

Complete with a video – where the Barry Met Man hitches a lift with a duck – Who the Heck is Derek? is a tongue-in-cheek re-make of the 70s Smokie hit Living Next Door to Alice. The song was also covered by mucky comic Roy Chubby Brown but luckily for 36-year-old Derek, none of his infamous swear words feature on

EXCLUSIVE

By LEAH OATWAY

the charity tune.

Mam-of-two Natalie Ball, from Cwm Parc, Treorchy, is the brains behind the new version, which stars Derek's BBC Wales Today newsreading pals. The 36-year-old was inspired to write the new lyrics by her eldest son Curtis, 10, who is crazy about the weather and the nation's favourite

BROCKWAY TRIES HIS DUCK: Natalie (inset) penned new song

weatherman.

A year after she sang her song down the phone to the BBC Wales Today newsdesk, Natalie is ecstatic it's made the telly.

She said: "It's amazing isn't it? I wrote it three weeks before Children In

Need last year but it was too late to do anything with. But I went away and wrote the full lyrics and this year it's ready to be shown!

"My eldest boy Curtis has always been a Derek fan – he wants his job when he grows up. He's really into the weather, has been for years.

"One day we were taking to someone and I mentioned his name and they said, 'Who the hell is Derek?'.

"I thought, 'That would make a wonderful song'!"

After singing the song down the phone to BBC Wales last year, Natalie bought the original song on CD and set to work. After bouncing a few ideas off Curtis and her younger son Alex, eight, Natalie's masterpiece was complete.

The video was filmed this week, billed as Wales

Today's own special tribute to Wales' national treasure – Derek Brockway.

It will be screened on Friday – the first time Wales Today presenters have performed for the BBC charity although national newsreaders have made it a tradition.

But you can relax – our source at the Beeb says it's a one-off.

"There are no plans to release it as a single as yet but sports presenter Bob Humphrys revealed such a good voice it sounded like he had been trained by the Welsh National Opera!" he revealed.

■ *leah.oatway@wme.co.uk*

BROLLY BOY: Curtis wants Derek's job

'Bean' a little down

HE MAY be orange but Captain Beany has admitted he's feeling blue.

Barry Kirk, who dresses up as the baked bean-loving superhero to raise money for charity, says he has been suffering from depression for the last four years.

It was triggered by the death of two close family members coupled with failing to raise as much money as promised at the New York marathon in 2001.

The mad-cap Port Talbot man now visits a psychiatrist and takes anti-depressants. Beany's speaking out to help break the taboo about mental health problems.

WEIRD

SIX South Wales firefighters have been named the best in the world at cutting casualties free from cars. Phil May, Mark Sanderson, Allyn Hosey, Simon Comely, Sean Cayford and leader Shaun Moody, from South Wales Fire and Rescue Service, were named World Extrication Champions 2005.

WALES

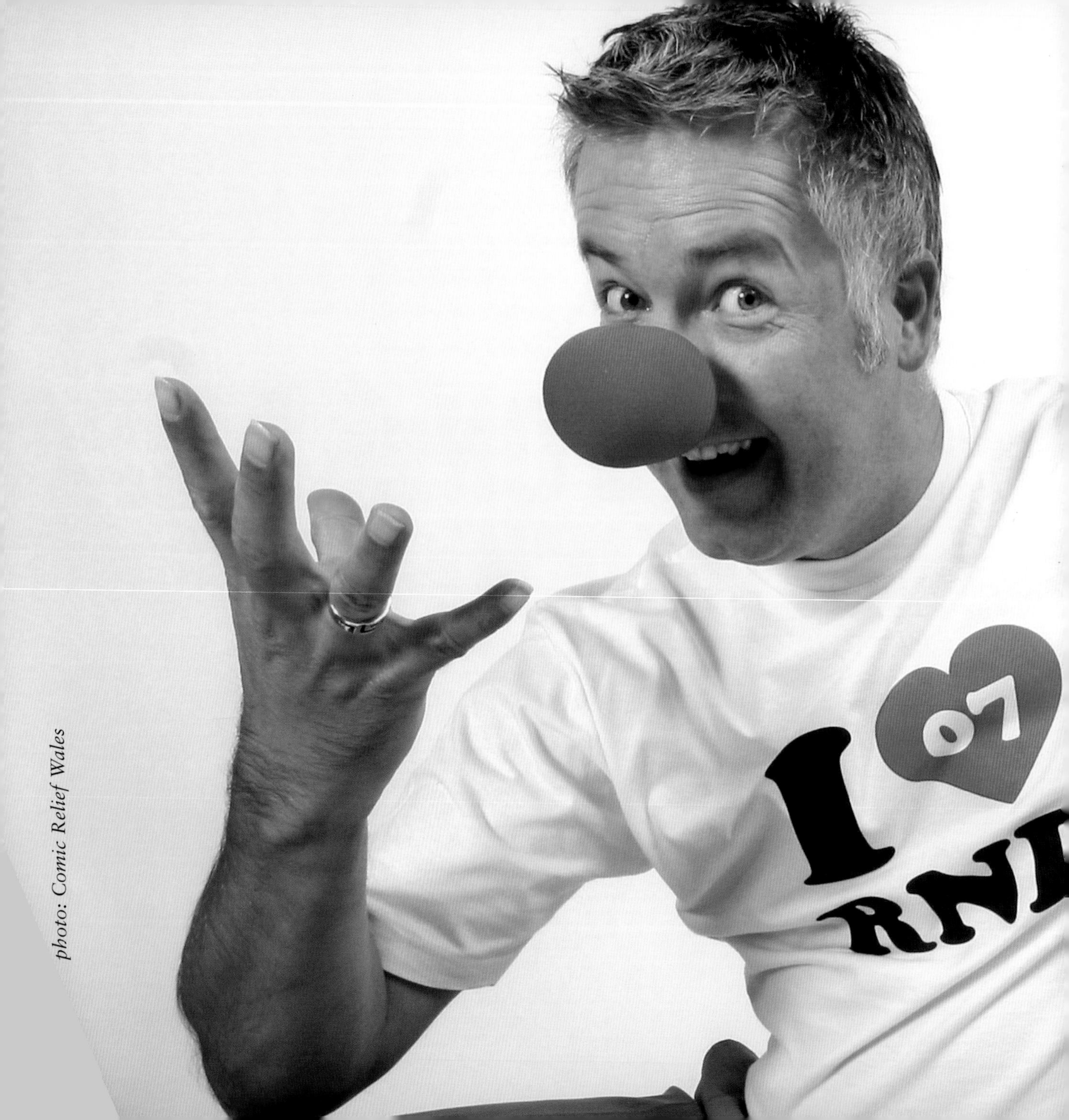

photo: Comic Relief Wales

Derek the Weather

Derek is our weatherman
He's such a jolly chap
Everybody is his fan
With arms a-waving at the map.

He tries so hard to soften the blow
If the weather's to be bad
And children's pictures he likes to show
He's such an all round good lad.

He'll dress up on the odd occasion
And join in all the fun
He receives many an invitation
To WI's or maybe a run.

He makes the weather entertaining
We look forward to his spot
We just don't care if it's raining
Snowing, blowing or even hot.

Come on Derek, strut your stuff
Forecasting for all of Wales
No matter if the weather's rough
Your accuracy never fails.

OUR DEREK

Derek our dear weatherman from wales you see
predicts the weather for the B.B.C with a cheerful
smile he beams with pride
He jumps around the studio with stride
With his arms so wide the weather is done in
seconds not minutes like the other side
He brightens things up when the weather is bleak
He's a cheerful chap all through the week
Rain again he will say not more rain Derek we pray
please please Derek say dry weather is on it's way
to keep my mother quiet for just one day

As a child, I knew I wanted to be a weatherman when I grew up but I never had a burning desire to work in television. Mind you, I suppose there was something there, some hidden ambition, because I can remember standing in front of the mirror in my bedroom sticking paper clouds on a map with blue-tak and pretending to deliver a weather forecast – a bit like most youngsters who sing in front of a mirror with a hairbrush for a microphone. In any case, my parents are happy that the rôle-play turned into a real career.

'We'll always be pleased with what you've achieved,' says Mum, 'proud of everything you've done in your life but it's just as important for us to know that, inside, you haven't changed one bit. Despite being on TV you're still the same person you always were.'

My father suffered a stroke several years ago and, unfortunately, it has taken its toll. He isn't the same man he used to be. He can't drive any more and Mum has become a full-time carer for him. It's very sad because they were looking forward to retirement and had intended to travel to so many different places. It makes me realise that you have to try and make the most of every day because you don't know what's around the corner. Work is important but I try and spend as much time as possible with my family and friends.

I enjoy my job, presenting on TV and radio, and have developed my own style. I tend to wave my arms around and occasionally bend my knees! Some people call me 'Dancing Derek'; others have said I should be in a West End show. I am not sure about that but I wouldn't mind doing a pantomime one day – maybe when I retire and have more time. Back in 2000, I received a letter from a viewer in Mountain Ash. He wasn't too keen on my arm-waving on screen and suggested I had fleas! What a cheek – but you have to laugh.

Most people appreciate what I do and some tune in especially to watch the weather forecast. One chap wrote to me and said his father suffers from depression but when he sees me on the television it lifts! It's nice to receive positive feedback and it's what keeps me going. Some people send birthday cards, write poems and a few have set up fan clubs such as the Derek Brockway Appreciation Society in Ruthin. Over the years, I have met some wonderful, kind and generous people in my travels across Wales. I receive invitations to give talks, open fêtes, festivals and have had the honour of switching on the Christmas lights in various towns such as Merthyr Tydfil, Cowbridge, Brynmawr and Pontypool.

Using a picture of 1947, sent in by a viewer, as part of the weather report

It is a great privilege to do the job I do, but it is not always easy being in the public eye. You do lose your privacy and part of me does yearn to be anonymous again. Some people call me a 'celebrity', a word I am not overly comfortable with, because at the end of the day I'm the boy from Barry who had an interest in the weather and has made a career out of his hobby.

The job has certainly changed since I started doing it in 1997. It's a lot busier now with eight radio and four television bulletins filling my day. But one thing has remained unchanged, and that's how important it still is for me to do a good job and to get the forecast right as often as I can.

A Day in the Life

In some ways, my life is a bit like the weather – no two days are ever quite the same. But many of the things I do follow a routine or pattern. One thing I am aware of as I get older is that I seem to be getting busier. There never seem to be enough hours in the day. However, I am well aware that all work and no play make Jack a dull boy so I try and have a good work-life balance. As Oscar Wilde said, 'Life is too important to be taken seriously.'

photo: Jo Manning

At my desk

Some people think I turn up to work at 5 in the afternoon, slap on some make-up and then pop up and present the weather at 6.55 in the evening before going home again. If only! There's a lot more to it than that. My alarm goes off at 7.45 in the morning, so I have a bit of a lie-in compared to most people. I normally wake up to *Good Morning Wales* on BBC Radio Wales or *The Today Programme* on Radio 4 with John Humphrys. The latter a sign, perhaps, that I am getting older! But I do like to listen to the forecast from the BBC Weather Centre at 3 minutes to 8; it gives me a head-up on what is happening.

After getting up, the first thing I do is look out of the window to check the weather. I think to myself, is the forecast I issued yesterday right or has it changed? If it's raining and I had forecast sunshine, which does happen every now and again, I get a sinking feeling and feel disappointment. I do take it personally and wonder how many people will notice; no one likes to get it wrong. But if the forecast is right I feel on cloud nine!

Sometimes if I am feeling energetic I will play squash before work but more often than not I leave exercise until after work and prefer a more leisurely start to the day. A quick shower followed by a bowl of porridge or a boiled egg and maybe a short burst of daytime TV. Each to their own, but I can never understand people who go to work on an empty stomach. I think of my body like a car; it needs fuel to make it go. If I'm on the road with work then I may treat myself to a fry-up but usually I try to avoid foods that are high in fat.

The drive to work takes less than twenty minutes and thankfully I miss the worst of the traffic. I get into the BBC around 10.30 in the morning and the first thing I do is switch on the computers. I try and limit myself to one cup of coffee a day, usually when I first get in to the office. Working in television under the lights and in radio studios is thirsty work so I drink plenty of water or herbal tea. I keep a bottle of water on my desk to avoid getting dehydrated. The last thing you want is a headache minutes before you go on air.

Once my computers are turned on, I look at a variety of information from the Met Office. I look at weather observations, analyse satellite and radar imagery, computer model data and read guidance from the Met Office. I also use the internet to study long-range charts. One of my favourite websites is www.greatweather.co.uk which has loads of information. This process allows me to build a picture of what the weather is doing in my head and then I can decide on the best way to tell the weather story for Wales on radio and television.

At 11.15am, I make a telephone call and dial into a special conference with the Chief Forecaster at the Met Office in

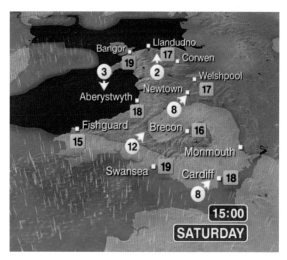

Television graphics need to be easily understood

Exeter. This link-up involves all the local forecasters across southern Britain and is chaired by someone from the national team in London. We discuss the forecast and whether or not we are happy with the TV graphics, what they are showing and if any changes are required to amounts of cloud, rain or snow.

The new style BBC graphics caused great controversy when they were first introduced in May 2005. There were complaints about the tilt and the brown colour of the map. People also missed the static weather symbols which had been in use for 30 years. No one likes change, including myself, and it took me a while to get used to the new system. The idea is to make the forecast clearer for the viewer at home. The brown shade used for the land was chosen because it is a neutral colour which emphasises the weather and reacts well to cloud and sunshine. Cloud is represented by darker shades on the map, while rain and snow are animated. I think the new graphics are a step forward; they are more realistic and quicker to use. They also save the forecaster time and are constantly evolving.

Claire Summers who often reads the lunchtime news

My first broadcast of the day is on Radio Wales on the Jamie and Louise show at about 11.45. Jamie refers to me as 'Our Chief Meteorologist,' and I call him Lord Owen. It's all good fun and just a bit of banter. I stay in the studio until the programme ends and normally Jamie comes back to me for a brief summary of the forecast. On Tuesdays there is often a chef on the show and we get to taste some of the food. Jamie makes out that I eat all the food but that's not true. At the end of the day, he's the one with the big belly, not me!

My relationship with Jamie has developed over the years, which is interesting in a way as we're a bit like chalk and cheese. I'm from a council estate in Barry and he went to a public school in Brecon. However, he's very helpful and encouraging, gives me a lot of advice and the jokes we share have become part of our friendship in and out of work.

After the radio show I head upstairs to pre-record the 14.45 radio bulletin and then I return to the office where I update the forecast, looking at the radar and the latest observations from around Wales. My next bulletin on Radio Wales is with Richard Evans at 12.45 and then I come back and have a look at the TV graphics, making any final changes. Then I head to the TV studio to prepare for the lunchtime news at 1.30 which is read by Sue Charles, Siân Lloyd, Jayne James, Claire Summers or Tomos Dafydd. I access my weather maps on the computer and then go through them and practise what I am going to say. After the lunchtime weather on television, I go back upstairs into the radio studio again for another update on the Richard Evans show.

It's interesting switching from radio to television and vice versa. They're totally different media. Television is very visual, of course. The first thing people notice is what you're wearing, how your hair looks, is your tie straight, that sort of thing. The words come later. I think women presenters get it in the neck more than men in terms of their clothes, hair and make-up. You have to have a thick skin otherwise it would get you down. On radio, it matters less how you look but speech is very important. People can't see me waving my arms so I have to speak clearly and engage the listener by using my voice!

On my way to the radio or television studio, I often take a quick look out of the window to check the weather and how the sky looks. Work colleagues find this funny and often joke about it, but observing is all part of the process and can lead me to change my forecast, if for example rain has arrived earlier than expected or the sun has come out.

If I'm lucky I manage to get myself some lunch in the BBC canteen just before it closes at 2pm. There is a good selection of food but normally I plump for a salad and it's a chance to relax with work colleagues. After lunch my next forecast on the radio is at 3.45pm with Roy Noble. Roy is very chatty and always makes me feel welcome. He is so knowledgable about Wales and the Welsh and has so many stories.

Roy Noble

After lunch I try and catch up with some admin and answer any letters or emails I may have received. It can be hectic at times, trying to balance all the various jobs, and I am constantly watching the clock so I am not late for my next broadcast. I guess I live on adrenalin most of the time, which can be tiring, but whatever I'm doing, forecasting the weather and presenting it on TV and radio are the most important parts of the job.

Throughout the day, I'm constantly updating myself with new information as it comes in from the Met Office. At 4 in the afternoon, there is another telephone conference with the Chief Forecaster where we discuss the latest output from the computer. After that, I may make a few tweaks to the forecast and then I'm on the radio at 4.25 and 5.25 on *Good Evening Wales*. I try to link

In make-up

the weather to how it will affect people's lives – how much impact rain or snow will have on their journey home in the rush hour. I also try to mention the odd sporting or social event as well, to make the forecast more personal.

Derek's Diary has become quite popular. People write to me or email details of local events or their photographs of the weather; anything that's interesting to my site – the email address is dereksdiary@bbc.co.uk – I try to use to add colour and character to the forecast. So, for example, if there's a summer fête taking place at a village in the middle of nowhere it can get a mention in one of my spots, time permitting of course.

I am often asked who decides on the place names on the weather map, well it's down to me. I try and change them every day for a bit of variety. Size isn't everything, though, and I often drop in names that are quite unexpected, the smaller the better. People love to see their town or village appear on the chart as it makes them feel part of the forecast and there are some great sounding names too like Rhosllannerchrugog and Penrhiwceibwr.

At about a quarter to five I head down to the make-up room and then it's into the studio to pre-record the short forecast that goes out after the late news at 10.30. It certainly isn't a live performance at that time of night, which can be a problem if the forecast changes! At 6.28 I deliver my final forecast on Radio Wales and then head to the television studio where I open up my weather graphics show on the computer. It takes a couple of minutes to load and I play it through a few times to make sure it's working properly. I then grab myself a sound pack and microphone and effectively wire myself up.

A formidable team

The evening news at 6.30 is presented by Jamie Owen, Claire Summers, Siân Lloyd or, until recently, Sara Edwards. It's a team effort and we all get on well. People like Bob Humphrys, Jason Mohammed and Sara have become more than colleagues and we enjoy the odd joke together. I often pull Jason's leg about his clothes. His suits are always immaculate and I reckon he must have his own shirt and tie shop in Ely, Cardiff. On one occasion, Sara asked me to provide a special forecast for her parents in Carmarthenshire. They were having a new Velux window fitted and wanted to know if the weather was going to stay fine. I was more than happy to give them a mention – all part of the job, as they say.

When I am on the radio I read from notes I have made, sometimes on the back of a brown envelope! Occasionally I will be told how much time to talk for but on the whole it's fairly relaxed, although Jamie does have an annoying habit of making gestures with his hands when he thinks I have waffled on for too long. I tend to ignore him and carry on!

Television is a different story, and there's much more pressure too. Everything I say is done from memory, off the cuff so to speak. I have a basic idea of what I want to say and my charts help tell the story. In some studios, the forecasters stand in front of a blue screen on which the weather graphics are projected. This gives them an idea of where to point but they can't wear blue clothes, otherwise they would disappear and all you would see is heads and

On location in Abergavenny

hands! In Cardiff, however, we use a plasma screen so I can wear blue if I want. I can also see myself and the maps in the camera in front of me.

While I am giving the forecast on television, someone behind the scenes is giving me a time-count in my ear. One minute, 30 seconds and then 10, 9, 8, 7, 6, 5, 4, 3, 2, 1 and I have to finish dead on zero. If I go over, this has implications for the newsreader because there is only a certain amount of time left until the end of the programme. The trouble is, the time I get does vary from day to day. In the evening I would normally expect about two minutes but it can be longer or, more usually, shorter, especially if a live interview has over-run. If this happens then I have to cut out chunks of what I was going to say, often at short notice. Sometimes I feel like the programme sponge, having to take up slack or else having to chop my piece to fit. It can be very frustrating when you have worked on something all day and then have to hack it to bits at the last minute. If you notice me suddenly speeding up when I am talking then that is a sure sign that my duration has been cut. I often have to fight my corner with the producer to protect my air time. I realise I have to be flexible but I just want to give the viewers the best forecast possible and not feel rushed. After all, the weather is a very important part of the programme and shouldn't be used as a filler.

Sometimes I am sent on location, especially during the summer months with the lighter nights and better weather. It's good to get out and about, and people seem to like to see me in their town or village, but Wales is a big place so it's difficult to get to some places without making it a very long day. It can also be a rush, preparing my charts and then driving through heavy traffic. When

I am on an outside broadcast, I rely on someone in the studio to change my charts and I can't see them when I do the forecast. I have to memorise the sequence, look at the camera and just talk until I'm told my time is up in my ear-piece.

Over the years I have presented the weather in various costumes and guises, like Guy Fawkes, an Italian chef, a Frenchman, a Welsh dragon and even Darth Vader! In December, I spice up the forecast by showing children's weather paintings in the run-up to Christmas. It's a good way of getting our younger viewers involved and hopefully taking an interest in the weather. It's very popular; I get inundated with pictures and often end up covered in glitter as I sift through them! Unfortunately, there isn't enough time to show them all, but for the children whose pictures are shown it's a very big deal indeed.

Once the evening news finishes at 7.00pm, that's it, I'm finished for the night. I go back to my office, switch off the computers and then head out to the car. Sometimes I may do some exercise or catch up with friends otherwise I go straight home. Occasionally there's a public engagement of some kind, but not too often in weektime, or else I'd never survive.

I don't think I've ever been quite as busy as I am now. It's a five-day week and the hours are long – not counting any other programmes like *Weatherman Walking* that I make. Extra programmes are often made at the weekends but I'm not complaining. I don't think I would want to do anything else. I know there are far harder ways to earn a living. I work with some great people and consider myself lucky to be in a job that I enjoy.

*Screen-grabs of my
dressing-up days*

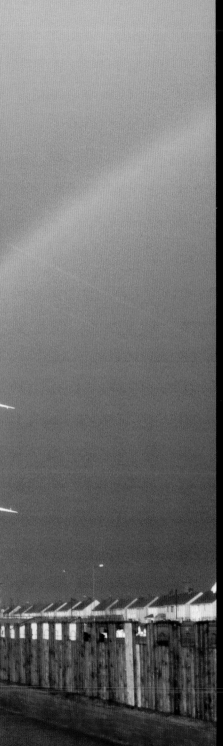

Climate change

Climate change is one of the most complex, interesting and controversial issues of our time. Over the past decade abnormal weather has made headline news in many parts of the world. The Stern Report and films such as *The Day After Tomorrow* and *An Inconvenient Truth* have helped put the subject well into the public spotlight.

All of us stand to benefit from rising to the challenge of climate change. It's the biggest threat to face modern civilisation and it would be both wrong and disastrous to ignore it.

Pontneddfechan falls in flood

It is easy to get weather and climate confused; they are interlinked but they are not the same thing. Weather is the state of the atmosphere at a given time and place, whereas climate is the average weather experienced over a longer period, typically thirty years. As Mark Twain said, 'climate is what you expect, weather is what you get.'

The climate of the Earth is constantly changing and has altered many times over millions of years due to a variety of natural causes such as major volcanic eruptions, changes in the Earth's orbit and output from the sun. Over the last 800,000 years there have been swings in temperature from cold to warm and back again leading to glacial and interglacial periods.

20,000 years ago Wales was covered by thick ice, while during the Middle Ages it was warm enough to grow grapes in northern England. This was followed in the 17th and 18th century by the Little Ice Age when winters were harsh and frost fairs were held on the river Thames in London. However, these were only regional phenomena. The problem now is that *global* temperatures are rising quickly and at a rate never experienced in recent history, which is causing great concern. Although part of this may be due to natural causes, it is thought that most of the warming, especially since the second half of the 20th century, is down to human activity such as the burning of fossil fuels – that is, coal, gas and oil.

The Earth has its own thermostat or natural greenhouse effect. The greenhouse gases include water vapour, carbon dioxide, ozone, methane and nitrous oxide. These natural gases help to keep us warm by trapping outgoing infrared heat from the Earth. Without them the Earth's average temperature would be about -15°C, everything would be frozen and life would be impossible!

Since the last Ice Age, the concentration of greenhouse gases in the atmosphere has remained nearly constant. However, since the Industrial Revolution, humans have been pumping out huge quantities of greenhouse gases, most notably carbon dioxide or CO_2. These act like a blanket over the infrared waves trying to escape from the Earth back into space, causing global warming. Levels of CO_2 are now much higher and increasing much faster than at any time in at least the last 650,000 years. Over the last 100 years, the Earth has warmed by approximately 0.75°C but about 0.4°C of this warming has happened since the 1970s.

20 of the warmest years have occurred in the last 25 years, so something is definitely happening. John Powell is an amateur weatherman who lives on the Gower peninsula near Swansea. He runs his own climate station and reports monthly to the Met Office. He also provides regular local weather forecasts on Swansea Sound radio.

John Powell, who was awarded an MBE in 1998 for his unbroken service to the Met Office over forty years

'I've been recording temperatures and rainfall for 46 years and records are tumbling all the time. Autumn 2000 was the wettest since records began in 1766. September 2006 was the warmest in Wales since 1914 and the whole Autumn of 2006 was the warmest I've ever known. In 2007 we had the warmest April on record and this was followed by a disappointing summer, the coolest since 1998, the wettest since 1912 – with severe flooding in June and July.'

Like most of us, John knows that it is difficult to pinpoint exactly why things are changing so quickly:

'There are so many possible reasons. We're shoving so much stuff into the atmosphere these days and that may be causing the problem, but then you've got to ask yourself are we just going through a natural warm period in the Earth's history?'

Traffic on the Neath valley road – how much CO_2 do we emit?

John may be right. The trouble is, climate is not something you can create in a test tube and climate prediction isn't an exact science. It is impossible to say exactly how the climate will change over the next hundred years because of the chaotic nature of the atmosphere. There are many uncertainties, due to unknown future greenhouse gas emissions, and other, natural, factors which may affect the climate in years to come.

Global warming will also cause some changes which may speed up further warming, such as the release of methane from the ground as permafrost melts in the tundra regions of the world. Other factors may offset warming; in a warmer climate plants will grow faster and may take more CO_2 from the atmosphere. One of the largest uncertainties is how clouds will respond to climate change. They could slow the warming down or speed it up. Scientists are not sure how the effects of these positive and negative feedbacks will balance out. However, most agree that computer modelling is the best tool for predicting what is going to happen in the future. The models are not perfect, but give us a guide to the direction of climate change, what the climate is most likely to do and what it probably won't do in the coming years.

Between 1940 and 1970 average global temperatures began to fall and some people thought the world was entering another ice age. Scientists now believe the cooling was caused by emissions of sulphate pollutants from industry and power stations, which tend to reflect sunlight. Before the days of central heating, coal fires were the only way to heat many homes and, combined with dense fog, the smoke from houses and factories created lethal smogs. The smogs became known as 'pea-soupers' because of their colour and thickness. In December 1952 a pea-souper in London killed more than 4,000 people but nobody realised what was happening until it was noticed that the undertakers were running out of coffins and the florists out of flowers! The Great London Smog galvanised the government to clean up the nation's air and the burning of raw coal was virtually banned. Consequently, more sunlight was able to reach the ground and temperatures began to steadily rise, revealing the true scale of global warming.

Scientists agree that the world climate is warming and most say the warming is probably due to us. The Intergovernmental Panel on Climate Change (IPCC) was set up in 1988 to evaluate the risk of climate change brought on by humans. In its latest assessment, it states world temperatures are likely to rise by between 1.1 and 6.4°C by the end of this century, depending on our emissions. And sea levels are expected to rise between 18 and 59 cm.

Hazel catkins even in January

Overleaf: Cwm Bowydd woods near Blaenau Ffestiniog
(photo: Jeremy Moore)

A warmer world means storms will have more energy which means stronger winds and heavier rain. There will be an increase in the severity and frequency of extreme events such as heatwaves, floods and droughts. Hurricanes will probably become more destructive in the future too.

The effects of climate change aren't going to be restricted to humans either. Animals, plants and trees are going to have to adapt as well. The seasons are changing. Spring is arriving in this country about two weeks earlier than it used to and autumn about a week or so later.

Dr Madeleine Havard is chief executive of the Wildlife Trust of South and West Wales. She acknowledges that climate change has been going on for thousands of years but is also clear that some strange things are happening in the natural world these days:

'What we're seeing now are some unusual variations in natural patterns. To start with, spring and summer flowers are now appearing in winter. We have catkins on trees in January, and willows in bud or even flowering at the beginning of the year. Daffodils are growing in some gardens as early as December and snowdrops before Christmas. I don't necessarily say that's good or bad, but it's a sure sign that our climate is on the change.'

Woodland on the banks of Rhaeadr Fawr, Snowdonia

The trouble is, as Madeleine says, all natural systems are inter-connected and if the pollinators, for example, are not available for the flowers which are flowering earlier than usual then it will have a huge impact for the future survival of some species.

'Without bees and other insects to carry the pollen, the natural processes of plant reproduction that have been going on for millions of years will get out of phase. Other changes also affect whole systems – we've had reports of frogspawn being found in garden ponds on 31st December. Normally frogspawn doesn't begin to appear until late January or early February. All it needs is a late cold snap and the developing frogs will not be able to survive. All nature is interconnected and species and systems are linked and dependent on each other, so if these links get broken, the long-term survival of certain species might be put into jeopardy, and all as a result of the changing weather patterns.

The changes are playing havoc with the budding times of trees. Oak, horse chestnut and sycamore are coming into leaf much earlier than usual. Other trees such as ash and beech could then be shaded out which will have a big impact on our woodlands. During the autumn, trees shed their leaves in response to falling temperatures and decreasing daylight but over the past few years there has been a change. In 2006, for example, sycamore trees lost their leaves much earlier than normal, probably due to drought and heat stress, but some ash trees retained their leaves for far longer than usual.'

Oak leaves

If trees are unduly stressed one year all their energy gets focused into reproduction and this can have an enormous effect on growth and foliage the next year. A warmer climate in Wales could mean that oak trees will fail to thrive.

'Our oaks do not like a hot, dry climate,' says Madeleine. 'If Britain's climate becomes more like the Mediterranean we would be able to grow orange, lemon and olive trees but this is not a comforting thought if it means the demise of trees like our native oak.'

What Madeleine and others are saying is that the changes in climate that we are now witnessing could possibly lead to a speeded-up process of evolution for

Snowdon lily

both plants and animals, a situation where those which adapt best to the new conditions survive, and others could die out altogether.

'I don't automatically say that all this is down to global warming,' says Madeleine, 'but it looks very likely. At the moment all we can safely predict is unpredictability, and we need to keep recording and collecting information about the changes happening in our environment.'

I have read that Snowdon could lose all its snow in less than 15 years, which would threaten rare plants like the Snowdon lily, which relies on hard winters to survive. Hywel Roberts from Gwynedd is a warden with the Countryside Council of Wales. He believes that climate change is already taking its toll in the Snowdonia National Park.

'Flowers such as the purple saxifrage are flowering earlier than normal and other vegetation which grows on the cliff ledges is under threat too. As the climate becomes less harsh, increasing numbers of mountain goats are able to climb higher and reach the cliff edges, threatening the survival of rare and fragile plants. Conservation organizations are trying their best to regenerate native broadleaved woodlands by preventing sheep from grazing, but the goats are able to get through the fences and cause a lot of damage.

Climate change is also affecting bird life. In the woodlands of Snowdonia the pied flycatcher which migrates to Wales from western Africa in the spring, has been returning earlier, and nesting 10 days earlier than in 1990. The breeding population has halved over the same period. It is also believed that the birds are returning to the woodlands in Wales to breed, producing eggs which hatch, but there is insufficient food present to feed the chicks because leaves for insects/larvae have not developed at the "normal" time.'

How much our climate will change depends upon our future greenhouse gas emissions. The UK Climate Impacts Programme (UKCIP) using data from the Met Office Hadley Centre predicts that Wales will become warmer. Summers will become drier and hotter with more heatwaves and an increased risk of drought. There may be difficulty providing adequate water supplies for parts of Wales during dry summers by 2025. Agriculture will need to adapt and there may be a move from livestock to arable farming in some parts of Wales, and a change in the crops grown. Irrigation may also be needed. Winters will become milder and wetter with more days of heavy rain and flooding. Snowfall will continue to decrease. More storms are likely too, with stronger winds and severe gales.

Some people will argue that a warmer climate in Wales would be a good thing, especially for tourism and agriculture. In winter there would also be fewer deaths from cold-related illnesses, but higher mortality rates are likely in the summer with a greater risk of heatwaves. In 2003 there were an estimated 2000 excess deaths in the UK and 30,000 across Europe because of the intense heat, especially among the sick and elderly.

Some poorer countries are already suffering from food shortages, drought and disease and some could disappear under water in the future, with millions of people in danger from flooding. Higher temperatures mean that glaciers and ice sheets will continue to melt and the oceans will expand. Warmer seas mean that more CO_2 will be released from the oceans to the atmosphere making climate change worse. There is also a risk that the ice covering Greenland could almost disappear in 3000 years time. If this were to happen, global sea levels would rise by around 7m on average and many major cities around the world, including Cardiff and Swansea, would be devastated.

As rainfall patterns around the world change, dwindling water resources could, together with depleted oil resources, become a potential source of future conflict. By the end of the century, rising sea levels and crop failures could create millions of refugees, leading to tension and war. Large numbers of animals face

Purple saxifrage

Texaco oil refinery, Pembroke

extinction and some plants could disappear altogether. Human health will suffer as well, with an increase in the spread of diseases such as malaria.

Wales is on the same latitude as Canada but because of the Gulf Stream our climate is warmer, annual mean temperatures are 9 degrees higher and we have milder winters. Scientists predict that if greenhouse gas emissions continue to increase, the Gulf Stream is likely to weaken. There is a small possibility it may switch off completely in the future. However, current computer predictions are confident that the effect of global warming will be greater, so a cooling of our climate is unlikely this century.

At the moment, most of our energy comes from fossil fuels and the amount of energy people use is increasing too, especially in developing countries like

China and India which are becoming more affluent as their economies grow. To stabilise climate change, emissions of CO_2 would have to be cut by 60 percent globally. Unfortunately this is not going to happen in the foreseeable future. Another thing to bear in mind is that CO_2 remains in the atmosphere for at least 50 years which means we are already committed to some degree of warming from our previous emissions. There is no going back in the short-term; we are already seeing change and will continue to do so. The damage our pollution today is causing will not take effect until later this century so we need to act now before it is too late.

Woodland in Nant Gwynant

Many governments around the world have signed the Kyoto Protocol, apart from the USA and Australia which have not ratified the treaty. However, this is not enough to stop climate change. We all need to do our bit to help reduce greenhouse gas emissions by cutting down on waste, recycling, making fewer journeys and saving energy. We must take responsibility for our own pollution, reduce our carbon footprint, and generate more electricity from renewable sources. Two billion tons of CO_2 enters the atmosphere every year from deforestation so we must stop chopping down the Earth's tropical rainforests.

If we sit back and do nothing, climate change will only get worse and some fear it could spin out of control, with disastrous consequences. The social, environmental and economic costs could be huge, as mentioned in the Stern report in October 2006. Only by acting together can we tackle the problems and save the planet for future generations to enjoy.

Leisure

What is this life if, full of care,
We have no time to stand and stare?

No time to stand beneath the boughs
And stare as long as sheep or cows:

No time to see, when woods we pass,
Where squirrels hide their nuts in grass:

No time to see, in broad daylight,
Streams full of stars, like skies at night:

No time to turn at Beauty's glance,
And watch her feet, how they can dance:

No time to wait till her mouth can
Enrich that smile her eyes began?

A poor life this if, full of care,
We have no time to stand and stare

With Sue Charles at Whitesands Bay

I've always liked that poem 'Leisure' by W. H. Davies from Pill in Newport. It's very simple but it sums up my attitude to life and to leisure quite nicely, and is very fitting for today's manic lifestyle. It is a reminder that we should take a break from our hectic and often stressful lives, switch off our computers and mobile phones and enjoy the simpler things in life. I could never imagine myself doing anything else other than working in the weather business for the Met Office – it gives me a lot of satisfaction. But there is more to life than work, and it is important to know when to stop and slow down.

Working in the media and doing a job that involves a degree of performance often causes an adrenalin rush. That makes it hard to 'come down' when you finish for the evening. So when I put the shutters up at 7.00pm I do find it hard to relax or switch off.

One thing that takes my mind off work is exercise. It's also a good way of releasing stress. I try to go to a boxercise class once a week with my colleague and friend Sue Charles. It's a mixture of exercises involving skipping, running, weights and boxing, with music playing in the background. Sometimes we go to the pub for a drink afterwards and Sue will buy crisps and occasionally order a plate of chips, undoing all our good work!

Sue thinks I am a real tinker. 'Derek has a funny sense of humour – a mixture of the naughty schoolboy and the *Carry On* films. He's always messing around, making noises and cracking jokes which are usually followed by filthy laughter that Sid James would have been proud of. You never know what he is going to say next. He's incorrigible!'

I do admit I can be a little outrageous at times and get away with murder with some of the comments I make, but as Kenny Everett used to say, 'It's all done in the best possible taste!' Or not, as the case may be.

I am lucky to have a good bunch of friends. Some of us meet regularly for 'TNT', which stands for Thursday Night Tuck. We turn up at someone's house with a dish we've made and have a wonderful feast followed by coffee, tea and organic chocolates. Afterwards we sometimes play games such as Twister or Pass the Parcel. We celebrate birthdays, Christmas and New Year together and occasionally go away on holiday. Bonfire Night is great fun too, when we all bring food and fireworks – mine is always the biggest and loudest!

Friendly youngsters at Whitchurch tennis club

I also enjoy squash and try to play at least once a week. I am not in a league or anything, just play for fun and to keep fit! It's a very fast sport, though, and not good for the knees. Another sport I am keen on, and would like to play more, is tennis. I was a member of Whitchurch Tennis Club in Cardiff for a while and would love to go to Wimbledon one day. I used to like watching Bjorn Borg and John McEnroe battle it out on centre court.

Some nights, if I am tired, I head home and try and have an early night. Maybe watch a bit of TV or read a book. I am one of these people who need eight to ten hours sleep a night but I rarely get that unless I am on holiday. The trouble is I have an over-active mind so I find it hard to switch off and relax. If I go to bed before midnight then I've done really well. Perhaps it's another sign of my restlessness. Mum tells me I was the same when I was young:

Skiing with Patrick Doohan

'You were always on the go and having fads. At one stage you were into baking and we had bread rolls and rock cakes all over the house. Then it was wine- and beer-making – huge demi-johns everywhere. And gardening, that was another craze. You laid two lawns at our old house and then went out and spent all of your father's money at the garden centre buying plants. The only thing that wasn't a fad was your interest in the weather.'

These days, I don't do much, if any, gardening but I do like to travel either here in Wales or abroad. Some of my work colleagues say I'm always on leave, while my friends reckon I have more holidays than Judith Chalmers! I wish that were true but travelling is one of my main interests. I like visiting different countries, discovering other cultures and climates. Plus when I am on holiday I find it easier to relax, and generally I sleep like a baby. There are so many places I would like to visit: New Zealand, Patagonia, Iceland, South Africa – the list is endless. I should have been a travel agent not a weatherman!

I also like skiing and first took to the slopes in 1987 with a colleague, Paul Davies, now a chief forecaster in Exeter. We went to Kitzbühel in Austria to try our luck. Since then I've skied almost every year, mostly in Europe but once in New England. I'd rate myself as an intermediate skier, someone who can tackle the odd black run but is more comfortable on reds and blues. A few years ago I was skiing in Italy and got a bit carried away, went too fast, lost control, fell and twisted my knee. I ended up in hospital and was off work for a while. BBC Wales sent a camera crew to my house and filmed me on crutches. Even now people ask me how my knee is! It's amazing the things people remember.

I often ski with one of my best friends, Patrick Doohan from Manchester. We've been mates for years and often go on holiday together. In 2004, we went around the world in a month. Our first stop was Denver, with skiing in Breckenridge, then it was on to Fiji via Los Angeles, then Australia. We went to Sydney, Ayers Rock, Cairns and finally flew to Hong Kong.

Carol Richards from Brecon is another good friend. We first met about five years ago in London and hit it off immediately. She is a first-language Welsh speaker and has really helped me with my Welsh. We both like walking and sometimes go travelling together; so far we have been to Glasgow, Prague, Milan and Alicante and always have a laugh.

With Carol Richards – my honeypot

'There's one distinct advantage of knowing a weatherman,' Carol says. 'If we're going on holiday I know what clothes to pack. Derek often talks about the weather which is handy because we know when to run for cover. He also tells me the names of clouds.'

The good thing about living in Wales is we have such beautiful countryside and beaches right on our doorstep. Carol and I often go walking in the Brecon Beacons, Snowdonia or in Pembrokeshire. I like a challenge and can proudly claim that I have climbed to the top of Ben Nevis in Scotland and to the very summit of Mount Teide in Tenerife. If I'm feeling more energetic sometimes I go mountain biking or wind surfing. I also like the Lake District and have recently been to Yorkshire, walking in the Dales. When I was in living in Birmingham, I passed my motorbike test. I have yet to buy my own but occasionally hire one when I am on holiday in the Greek Islands.

Mind you, another place I've discovered is Barbados. It's so beautiful and the people are very friendly and laid-back. I was only there for a week but travelled around in a jeep and on the Rasta buses the locals use – you just stick your hand out and flag them down. It's a good way of seeing the island, mixing with the locals and listening to reggae music.

With Michelle Hatcher in New York

A few of us went on a catamaran boat trip which involved sailing up the coast with a couple of stops to go swimming with turtles. There were unlimited free drinks on board so most people, especially the Brits, were happy to take full advantage. Suddenly a tropical storm blew up, with gusty winds and torrential rain. It was like being in a power shower. I'll never forget one woman trying to look dignified as the rain relentlessly beat down on top of her. Most people on board found the whole situation hilarious. It was a first-hand lesson in the power of nature. I've only been to Barbados once but I hope very much to return one day soon. The beaches were stunning and the sea so warm and clear.

Being on television I often get recognized when I'm 'off duty' – in the street, supermarket, pub or restaurant, anywhere really. Most of the people I meet are friendly and polite, they just want to say hello, shake your hand or have a chat. Some ask for an autograph or want a photograph with me. I don't mind because I know it comes with the job and for some it's a big deal to meet someone they consider famous off the box. However, there are always those who go a step too far. I was heckled in a restaurant once and some people come up to me when I am eating a meal. I can find myself feeling quite uncomfortable at times because you can't always be sure how people are going to react. All it takes is one person to say or do something unfortunate and an evening out can be ruined, but by and large most people are lovely.

Sometimes I try to disguise myself, wearing a hat and sunglasses but even that doesn't always work. My distinct Barry accent often gives me away! There are days when you want to be left alone and one of the reasons I go on holiday is to get away from it all. I can be myself and people don't know anything about me and vice versa. Mind you, going

Barry lifeguards – new recruits

abroad brings no guarantees and I have been spotted in Greece, Ibiza and Perpignan! It makes me realise how some people in the public eye end up becoming reclusive.

These days I don't go swimming much unless I am on holiday, but I used to go more often when I was in school. I won an Intermediate Award and for a while I even thought of becoming a lifeguard in Barry. I started to train but I nearly drowned when they threw me into the pool dressed in my pyjamas, so that put an end to that! During the 1970s my family and I used to go to the outdoor pool at Cold Knap in Barry. It's such a shame it had to been demolished as we had some wonderful times there. In my late twenties I was a member of Cardiff Dragons' Swimming Club, and used to train in the Empire Pool. It's one of the best ways of keeping fit because the water supports your body and limbs.

The important thing for me is to stay active. I've never been the type of person to sit still for long, staying in and watching television all day or night,

Gliding – a chance to see clouds close-up

though I quite like going to the cinema or theatre every now and again. I am always on the go, seeing friends or playing sport. I tend to keep going until my body tells me it's time to slow down.

I have to be careful because it's easy to get over-tired and then of course you're more likely to fall ill with some bug or infection. In May 2006 I went down with the dreaded chicken pox, which can be really nasty for an adult. I was covered in spots and my face looked as if it had been exposed to a nuclear experiment that had gone badly wrong. For a while, I was concerned that it could be the end of my career in television. I was off work for nearly a month and had to rest and do nothing. Thankfully, the spots healed but they have left a few dents in my face. Anyone who works in the media tends to live life on the edge, rushing here, there and everywhere. It's so easy to burn out if you're not careful.

If ever I'm off ill, someone has to fill the gap and that's not easy at short notice. I am the only broadcast meteorologist based in Cardiff; the others are miles away in London. So unless I am on planned leave, cover is provided in the form of a pre-recorded forecast sent down the line from the BBC in London. I've always felt it's important for me to stay fit. You can't broadcast effectively if – no pun intended – you're under the weather!

I was talking to Mum about that the other day:

> 'If ever you're not on TV for some reason,' she said, 'some of my friends will be on the phone before I know it asking "Where is he? He's not on today. He's not on holiday again, is he?" I get to know if you're ill long before you actually get round to telling me!'

It is hard to switch off. Even if I'm walking in the hills or on holiday I'm always thinking about the weather, looking up at the sky, wondering what's going to happen next. I always try to catch the forecast wherever I am, either on Radio 4 or on the television.

One of my dreams is to take part in an exchange with a weather forecaster from another country, maybe Australia or the USA. I bet the Americans would love my Welsh accent!

I like listening to music, especially when I'm driving or in the house working on the computer. I like a variety of stuff from classical, pop, jazz and even rock; bands like Rush, Cold Play, Snow Patrol, the Kaiser Chiefs and White Snake; it depends on what mood I'm in. I've seen Madonna, Michael Jackson, Blondie,

Charity Ball with Bonnie Tyler

Duran Duran, The Rolling Stones and Depeche Mode in concert over the years and hope to see The Police this year as well. I've also seen Tom Jones and Shirley Bassey and have met Bonnie Tyler and Katherine Jenkins, who is really down to earth. I've also had the pleasure of meeting David Tennant and Billie Piper who were in Cardiff to switch on the Christmas lights. I had to hide inside the Tardis with Claire Summers from BBC Wales, then we came out and spoke to the crowds. It was good fun and David and Billie were really friendly.

When I was young, I did learn to play the flute when I was in school and once went around people's houses playing Christmas carols. They seemed to like the sound I made – at least I didn't get any tomatoes thrown at me! Mum tells me that people used to say 'Play some more'. I don't know how good I was but my music teacher wanted me to carry on with the lessons. However, for one reason or another I gave it up. I guess it was another one of those interests that teenagers have that don't last. It's a shame really, because it's good to be able to read music and have another string to your bow.

Despite loving my job I always look forward to Friday. Colleagues in work say my behaviour changes and that I often become louder. It's excitement, I guess,

A Brockway family reunion

the same buzz that made me keep asking 'Are we there yet?' from the back seat of the car when we were off on holiday all those years ago. Like most people who work Monday to Friday, I look forward to the weekend, knowing that I've got two days away from the routine.

It's rare for me to have nothing planned at all. Sometimes I go away for the weekend, perhaps to London or Manchester, other times I stay at home. I like to potter around the house and catch up with a few chores. On a Saturday afternoon, I often visit my parents in Barry and take Mum and Dad out to lunch. My brother and sister both live in Barry too and occasionally the whole family will meet up on Sunday for a roast dinner at a pub.

On a Saturday night, I often go out into Cardiff with friends, go to the cinema or out for meal. On Sundays I try and have a lie-in but if the weather is good I may go walking or play tennis. It's a good way of clearing your head, especially if you've had too much wine the night before! Other times, I may meet up with friends for breakfast in Pontcanna and then afterwards I may pop into town for some retail therapy. The shops are not so busy on a Sunday. And then, before I know it, Sunday evening is here, it's time to get ready for work and do some ironing. Mind you, Monday doesn't hold any horrors for me. In fact, after a busy weekend, it's often a relief to get back into the swing of things.

My life is sometimes like a merry-go-round and that's why it's important to enjoy those moments when I'm off duty. Mum says 'You're always on the go. Why don't you stay in more often and relax?' I do try and have the odd night in but have a habit of 'arranging things', so before I know it my diary is filling up. At the end of the day, it's good to spend as much time as possible with friends and family, enjoy the countryside, laugh and have fun as well. We're not on this planet long, after all, so let's make the most of it!

Dribbling on Barry Island!

photo: Eric Keen

Meeting the Audience

Since the advent of television in the 1950s, weather forecasters have become personalities in their own right. Ian McCaskill, Bill Giles, Michael Fish – who can forget their daily appearances after the news? They each had their own style, something that made them different, and the British public took them to their hearts. One of them, John Ketley, even had a song written about him – 'John Kettley is a Weatherman' by the Tribe of Toffs.

With former S4C weathergirl Jenny Ogwen at the National Eisteddfod

It's hard to know exactly why forecasters have become TV personalities. Maybe it's something to do with the fact that, deep down, most of us are creatures of habit. So to come home from work, switch on the television and see a familiar face giving out their words of wisdom about the weather is somehow comforting and makes everything alright.

But an even more fundamental reason for the public's interest in weathermen is the national obsession with weather. When two people bump into each other, perhaps at the bus stop, it's the first topic of conversation. And when you think about it, it's not surprising; the weather affects everything we do – how we feel, what we wear and even what we eat and drink.

The famous Dr. Samuel Johnson, who wrote the first proper English dictionary, said it all: 'It is commonly observed, that when two Englishmen meet, their first talk is of the weather; they are in haste to tell each other, what each must already know, that it is hot or cold, bright or cloudy, windy or calm.' And the Welsh are no different, of course.

Our fascination with the weather has become almost a cliché and the reason is down to the fact that our weather is very changeable. No two days are ever the same and you can have all four seasons in one day. However, instead of moaning about the weather – or blaming it on the forecaster like me – we should be grateful for our temperate climate.

You could say that the climate of the British Isles has helped make us the people we are – hardy, eager to get on with our daily lives regardless of the elements. The weather has protected our islands over the years, keeping invaders at bay and creating an environment where crops can grow and animals can be reared in relative peace and quiet.

At the moment most people in Wales seem to like what I do. I'm told that wives will shout to their husbands, 'Quick, Derek's on,' and then they'll sit together watching the forecast! However, I am aware that the media is fickle and although I may be popular now, things can change, sometimes quickly, and I could be out on my ear tomorrow.

I do try and make my weather forecasts – and, indeed, all my appearances on TV – as interesting as possible. I've been allowed to develop my own style over the years. I know I can be flamboyant at times, which is part of the act, but I hope my enthusiasm for my subject shines through. A forecast is all about information, education and entertainment. The first two almost speak for themselves but the last point is just as important. It's no good having the best researched weather forecast in the world if people switch off or fall asleep the moment you open your mouth. You have to keep people's attention otherwise there is no point in being there – the news anchor might as well read out the forecast!

I don't know about you, but I sometimes feel that there is too much 'dumbing down' in our society these days. And that's one of the reasons why I try and include things like the synoptic chart in my presentation, showing areas of high and low pressure and fronts which can help to tell the story. Not everybody understands them but many do and for those who don't, it might encourage them to find out. It's all about keeping the viewers happy, giving them want they want and hopefully making them smile. I try and put a positive slant on things and I have been told that I make bad weather sound better.

It's nice to receive feedback and occasionally I get emails and letters from the public. Mags Owen from Borth is often in touch. She tells me what the weather is doing in her back garden, which can be useful. Most people are polite but you can't please everyone and there will always be those who are quick to spot a mistake and tell you about it.

It's strange sometimes when I look back on the way my life has gone. I can't say that I ever thought about appearing on television, let alone writing books, when I was in school. We all have our dreams but it's not often that they come true. I suppose I have always under-estimated myself; even now I think that I haven't really achieved that much.

I have never been the type to actively seek extra work. People at the BBC approach me with ideas and I just respond to them. Despite what you might see

With photographer Mike Davies, who often sends me spectacular weather shots

Meeting fellow weather-watchers

on television I'm not a pushy person and have never been good at selling myself. I have a degree of confidence which you need to go in front of the camera, but I also suffer from bouts of self doubt.

My agent, Sheila Willicombe, is always telling me, 'Derek it's about time you realised just how "in demand" you are!' I'm still not convinced. As far as I'm concerned I am Derek Brockway, the boy from Barry who just happens to be on TV. Hopefully, whatever I do in the future, my feet will stay firmly on the ground. Forecasting the weather is my bread and butter job, of course, but it's also nice to be given the opportunity to make other programmes for television and radio – the chance to be creative and develop new skills.

I had my first radio series back in 2001, *Derek's Lightning Guide to the Weather*, and this was followed in 2004 by a television series called *Derek's Welsh Weather*, which I really enjoyed making. In 2002 Penny Arnold, a producer at BBC Wales, came up with the idea of a radio series called *Weatherman Walking*, which combines my love of the weather with walking and the countryside. This was subsequently turned into a television series which was shown in early 2007 and a book was published as well. Lots of people watched, the ratings were good so BBC Wales asked for another series. The good thing about making such programmes is that I get to see some beautiful places, learn more about the history of Wales and meet some wonderful people along the way as well.

Recently Jamie Owen and I presented a series of family concerts called 'Weather and Water' with the BBC National Orchestra of Wales. The first two concerts took place at St David's Hall, Cardiff and Sir Thomas Picton School, Haverfordwest. I came on stage wearing a sou'wester, waterproofs and wellies which was all part of the fun. It was a little nerve-wracking appearing in front of such a large audience but after a while I got used to it and the butterflies disappeared. The audience really enjoyed themselves and hopefully learned more about the weather as well as classical music. Jamie and I have also worked recently on a new television series called *Jamie and Derek's Big Welsh-Weekends* for BBC Wales. We travelled around Wales, meeting people, having fun and trying different activities such as mountain biking, coracle fishing and horse riding.

A few years ago I did a stint as a disc jockey on Radio Wales, standing in for Kevin Hughes. I had never done anything like that before in my life so it was an interesting experience. I even got to play a few records for my friends. I've also

Margaret Brown, a loyal fan

been involved in the BBC Wales *Here for You* roadshows which have been touring Wales. People get the chance to meet some of the presenters and even have a go at reading the weather. It's good to get out and about, visiting different communities and meeting the locals.

One of my biggest fans is Margaret Brown, a lovely lady from Cardiff. I first met her after giving a talk to the local Women's Institute. She buys me gifts and occasionally bakes me a cake which is very kind. I do lots of public appearances but I must confess to preferring the one-to-one chats rather than talking to a big audience. When you stand in front of a camera or sit in front of a microphone thousands may be watching or listening but you can't see them. However, it's a different story when speaking in person to a large group, with all those faces looking at you. I try to help out when I get asked to give a talk, an after-dinner speech or take part in a fashion show. It can be hard being in the public eye all the time but it goes with the job, and the more you do the easier it gets.

Weather
and Water

All dressed up at the Lammas Fayre in Pont-lliw

And undressed on a charity calendar for Autism Cymru

Some people ask if I've ever had any embarrassing moments. Well, there have been a few over the years. I was reading the weather from an open-top bus in Cardiff during the Rugby World Cup in 1999. I was waffling on about wet and windy weather when suddenly the huge umbrella that I was sheltering under was caught by a strong gust of wind and was hurled like a javelin across the road. Thankfully no one was hurt but a clip of me was shown on the BBC programme *Auntie's Bloomers*. On another occasion, I was presenting the weather in studio, got slightly over-excited and stood on the cable connected to my chart changer. I picked it up and said, 'Excuse me, I seem to have dropped my plunger!' The thing is, when you are broadcasting live you have to be prepared, because *anything* can go wrong without warning. You just have to think on your feet.

In 2005 I took part in a TV series called *The Big Welsh Challenge*. The learners, myself included, had to complete several tasks using the Welsh language in different situations. I have an 'O' level in Welsh from my school days so I wasn't a complete beginner but it's amazing how much you forget over the years. Siân Lloyd from ITV was my mentor on the show. Her teaching style raised a few eyebrows at first but she got better as time went on and gave me a lot of encouragement, especially for my final challenge which was to present the weather in Welsh on S4C. It was one of the hardest things I've ever done, but afterwards I felt a great sense of achievement. I would love to be fluent in Welsh one day; it's a wonderful language and opens the door to a wealth of culture and history. Trying to find time for lessons is not always easy but there are some great resources available to learners these days, including the internet, and I am fortunate to know a lot of Welsh speakers so I can practise on them.

Of course, technology is developing all the time and the way we watch television is going to change in the future. By 2012, the analogue TV signal will be switched off and the whole country will have to be 100% digital. This means many more channels and interactive features – and picture quality will improve as well. New services will be delivered on different 'platforms' such as the internet and mobile phone. Television 'on demand' will allow you to watch what you want when you want. Local TV may also be rolled out across the UK. You can already download a small version of me from the internet. Desktop Derek sits on your computer screen and gives an indication of the weather conditions around Wales. You never know, one day I may be replaced by a virtual Derek generated by a computer. Personally, I hope this is some way off, but nothing stays the same for ever and with new technology, the way we live and work is going to change in years to come.

Somebody asked me the other day what I wanted to do in the future, whether I want to follow in Helen Willett's footsteps and become a forecaster on national television. Well, I am not sure they would have me in London, but to be honest my heart is in Wales. Most of my friends and family live here and I am lucky to have a job that I enjoy. I've been called the face and voice of Welsh weather and I can't see myself doing anything else. If the TV and radio work ended tomorrow, which is possible, I would find it hard to work behind the scenes again but one thing is for sure, my love of the weather would continue.

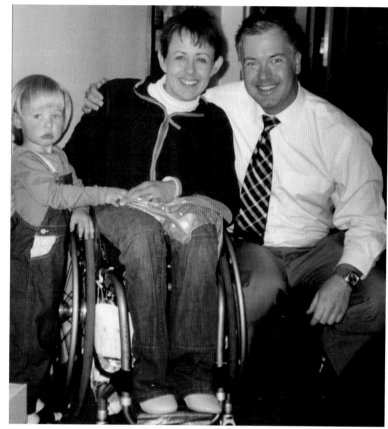

Dame Tanni Grey-Thompson, a fellow Welsh learner, with her daughter Carys

Siân Lloyd – quite a tutor